$ 899

PATIENT CHART

Patient: Tony Swan, age 8

Psychologist: Dr. Leslie Roarke

Findings: Tony can't read or write, but his photographic memory can spot a picture hanging half a millimeter off center. His speech is baby babble—usually a high, intense level approaching a scream—but he can sing an entire aria without missing a note after hearing it only once. He can't recognize numbers but can solve complex puzzles.

Despite all this, Tony somehow gets to the heart of the matter. He seems to <u>know</u> things. Maybe he can teach me how to deal with Michael Bradshaw?

Dr. Leslie Roarke

1. ALABAMA
Late Bloomer—Peg Sutherland
2. ALASKA
Casey's Flyboy—Vivian Leiber
3. ARIZONA
Second Wife—Stephanie James
4. ARKANSAS
Bittersweet Sacrifice—Bay Matthews
5. CALIFORNIA
Hunter's Way—Justine Davis
6. COLORADO
Rafferty's Choice—Dallas Schulze
7. CONNECTICUT
Special Delivery—Judith Arnold
8. DELAWARE
Taking Love in Stride—Donna Clayton
9. FLORIDA
Marriage by the Book—Joan Johnston
10. GEORGIA
Baby, It's You—Celeste Hamilton
11. HAWAII
Daddy's Girl—Barbara Bretton
12. IDAHO
One of the Family—Kristine Rolofson
13. ILLINOIS
Above Suspicion—Andrea Edwards
14. INDIANA
Intrusive Man—Lass Small
15. IOWA
Count Your Blessings—Kathy Clark
16. KANSAS
Patchwork Family—Carla Cassidy
17. KENTUCKY
Heart's Journey—Cathy Gillen Thacker
18. LOUISIANA
Crazy Like a Fox—Anne Stuart
19. MAINE
Fantasies and Memories—Muriel Jensen
20. MARYLAND
Minor Miracles—Rebecca Flanders
21. MASSACHUSETTS
Only the Nanny Knows for Sure—Phyllis Halldorson
22. MICHIGAN
The Proper Miss Porter—Ruth Langan
23. MINNESOTA
Emily's House—Nikki Benjamin
24. MISSISSIPPI
Beloved Stranger—Peggy Webb
25. MISSOURI
Head Over Heels—Leigh Roberts

26. MONTANA
Renegade Son—Lisa Jackson
27. NEBRASKA
Abracadabra—Peg Sutherland
28. NEVADA
Chances—Janice Kaiser
29. NEW HAMPSHIRE
Racing with the Moon—Muriel Jensen
30. NEW JERSEY
Romeo in the Rain—Kasey Michaels
31. NEW MEXICO
Desperate Measures—Paula Detmer Riggs
32. NEW YORK
Honorable Intentions—Judith McWilliams
33. NORTH CAROLINA
Twice in a Lifetime—BJ James
34. NORTH DAKOTA
Letters of Love—Judy Kaye
35. OHIO
One to One—Marisa Carroll
36. OKLAHOMA
Last Chance Café—Curtiss Ann Matlock
37. OREGON
Home Fires—Candace Schuler
38. PENNSYLVANIA
Thorne's Wife—Joan Hohl
39. RHODE ISLAND
Somebody's Hero—Kristine Rolofson
40. SOUTH CAROLINA
The Sea at Dawn—Laurie Paige
41. SOUTH DAKOTA
Night Light—Jennifer Greene
42. TENNESSEE
Somebody's Baby—Marilyn Pappano
43. TEXAS
The Heart's Yearning—Ginna Gray
44. UTAH
Wild Streak—Pat Tracy
45. VERMONT
MacKenzie's Baby—Anne McAllister
46. VIRGINIA
First Things Last—Dixie Browning
47. WASHINGTON
Belonging—Sandra James
48. WEST VIRGINIA
The Baby Track—Barbara Boswell
49. WISCONSIN
Fly Away—Pamela Browning
50. WYOMING
The Last Good Man Alive—Myrna Temte

Please address questions and book requests to: Harlequin Reader Service
U.S.: 3010 Walden Ave., P.O. Box 1325, Buffalo, NY 14269
CAN.: P.O. Box 609, Fort Erie, Ont. L2A 5X3

MARYLAND

REBECCA FLANDERS

Minor Miracles

Harlequin Books

TORONTO • NEW YORK • LONDON
AMSTERDAM • PARIS • SYDNEY • HAMBURG
STOCKHOLM • ATHENS • TOKYO • MILAN
MADRID • WARSAW • BUDAPEST • AUCKLAND

HARLEQUIN BOOKS
225 Duncan Mill Road, Don Mills,
Ontario, Canada M3B 3K9

ISBN 0-373-47170-X

MINOR MIRACLES

Dear Reader,

We all dream of winning the lottery, traveling the world on our private yachts, or retiring to a luxury villa by the sea. But sometimes the best miracles are the minor ones: the parking space that opens up just when you need it, the rainstorm that doesn't come until *after* you've unloaded the groceries, the smile of a child.

I hope you enjoy the story of Michael, Leslie and Tony, and the miracle of love that changed their lives.

Best,

Rebecca Flanders

Chapter One

Leslie Roarke sat very still, focusing all her attention upon the man who worked on the other side of the two-way mirror, unaware of his hidden audience. On either side of her, Leslie's colleagues occasionally shifted restlessly or cast furtive, questioning glances at her, but Leslie did not allow herself to become distracted. She was mesmerized—not so much by what she saw on the other side of the mirror, but by what she was afraid she would not see if she for one minute looked away.

His name was Michael Bradshaw. He was thirty-six years old, but looked perhaps ten years younger. He was, in fact, a most unusual-looking man in all respects. He was a study in shades of brown and gold; thick, shaggy hair the color of pale champagne and streaked with hints of sunshine was brushed carelessly away from a high forehead. In concentration, as he was now, his deep-toned brows formed an almost perfect V over the bridge of a sharply defined nose, accenting a face that was smooth and tanned and completely unmarred by lines of worry or age. His face was sharply shaped, each feature distinctly defined and individually memorable, combining to form a visage that was at the same time gaunt and beautiful, innocent and dangerous, sensitive yet impenetrable. His was a face that could not be replicated and could never be forgotten, and it bore the stamp of a man not easily categorized by anyone.

ual physical characteristic of
yes. They were the most strik-
eslie had ever seen in a human
that, more than anything else,
a huge, tawny cat when she
e sheer beauty invited caresses,
radiated a warning. As deter-
o regard him with nothing more
nal judgment, it was his physical
appearance m... ..ything else that inspired a dim and
unpreventable sense of awe.

In the past hour Leslie had watched as Michael Bradshaw, through nothing more than the force of his will, dissolved a link in a heavy iron chain, twisted a silver serving
spoon into an unrecognizable lump of metal with a few
light strokes of his fingers, caused a glass of water to boil
without any apparent source of heat, and extracted a shrill
ringing from a telephone whose cord had been neatly sev-
ered in two. In another room one of the staff had been
sealed inside with nothing but a map of Italy, upon which
he concentrated until Michael Bradshaw reproduced the image—in the form of an unmistakable drawing of a boot.

Now Michael sat at a sturdy Formica table in the center
of the room, his hands folded on the tabletop, focusing
intently upon a small vacuum-sealed glass case before him.
Inside the case was a light bulb attached to a simple battery
compound—the kind every child learns to make in junior
high school science class, but with one notable exception.
Between the battery and the light bulb there was no con-
ductor. According to the known laws of physical science,
there was no way that the light bulb inside the sealed case
could possibly produce light.

Michael had been staring trancelike at the case, motionless for over five minutes. The faint, slow sound of his
breathing was audible over the open microphone. He hardly
seemed to blink, and in the intensity of his concentration a
sheen of perspiration had formed on his face, beading a bit
around his eyes and glistening in dewy droplets on the

swooping V of his eyebrows. Leslie could feel the tension mounting in her own body, pulling for him, trying to help him—which was ridiculous, of course. It was only the suspense, and the awful stillness of waiting.

On her right, George murmured, "He's tired."

Malcolm, on her left, shifted his ample bulk uncomfortably in a hard plastic chair and agreed, "I don't think he'll make this one. When we tried it yesterday, he was fresh. He's been at this for over an hour."

George said, "What's his bio?"

Malcolm tilted his half glasses down on his nose as he leaned forward to check the electronic monitor that kept a constant record of Michael Bradshaw's pulse, respiration and temperature. "Stable. Respiration twelve, pulse forty."

The two scientists shared a glance across Leslie that didn't register undue concern over the fact that Michael's vital functions were almost forty percent below the norm. But Leslie found it more difficult to be blasé. She had never liked the two-way mirror technique, and couldn't get used to the feeling that those on the other side of the mirror were being dehumanized in some way—the victims, more than the voluntary subjects, of scientific research. Besides, their present volunteer was beginning to look a little pale to her; the flesh across his high cheekbones seemed tauter, and perspiration was dotting his upper lip.

Leslie said, without taking her eyes off Michael Bradshaw, "Five more minutes. Then we call it off. And, Malcolm, watch his respiration. It sounds like it's slowing to me."

"Just a fraction. Still within acceptable limits." He flashed her a grin. "Not to anyone but us, of course. No one outside this room would believe that a man could consciously slow his pulse and respiration down to half—and still remain conscious."

"A man can also consciously give himself a heart attack," snapped Leslie. "And that is *not* the purpose of this experiment. Watch him."

George said softly, "Well, I'll be damned."

Inside the glass cage the filament of the light bulb had begun to glow, gently, almost imperceptibly. Leslie caught her breath and leaned forward slightly in the booth. Michael's hands were clenched tightly together now; she could see a small quiver in the muscles of his arms with the force of the strain. His breathing began to quicken. The light bulb flickered, and glowed again, more strongly now. It was impossible, but it was happening. And Michael Bradshaw was doing it.

His eyes narrowed intently, perspiration bathing his face. Michael focused on the light bulb and its brilliance grew brighter and brighter, until its wattage made his skin seem almost translucent, his eyes shimmering slits of gold. And then, abruptly, having reached the pinnacle of effort, Michael released a huge breath, his body went slack, and the light bulb dimmed and went out. He slumped back in his chair, drained.

The silence among the three scientists was attenuated. Malcolm, after a moment's stunned paralysis, quickly began to check the vital-sign readings that poured at a steady rate from the machine, but he seemed to have temporarily lost his voice and could only nod reassurance to Leslie's anxious look. George, momentarily stripped of the live-wire energy that was his trademark, could only whisper limply, drawing out each syllable to its fullest, "All...*right*." And the three of them sat there, staring at the slowly recovering purveyor of the paranormal on the opposite side of the mirror, trying in their separate ways to resign their scientific minds to what they had undeniably seen with their own eyes.

Leslie would not have been inside this building were she not possessed of an open mind. Her business, her dedication, her absorbing interest, was the exploration of the unexplained. Even in the most orthodox aspects of her profession, she faced the impossible every day; the supernatural and the paranormal were only an extension of the mysteries of the human mind.

Yet the very essence of a scientist was skepticism and

she was not easily impressed; the nature of her work had taught her over the years that there was no such thing as the unexplained—only answers that had not yet been found. She did not believe in miracles; she shared neither the awe nor the excitement that was at this moment coursing through her two colleagues. It would be foolish to deny the fact that Michael Bradshaw was an extraordinary find, but he was nothing more and nothing less than a puzzle waiting to be assembled by her dexterous fingers. She had met such challenges before. Then why did her knees feel so weak as she got slowly to her feet?

"Well," she said, then she had to clear her throat to maintain the proper light tone of voice. "I'm gone two weeks and this is what happens. Congratulations, boys. He's quite…impressive."

As though injected with adrenaline, George recovered himself with a jolt. His wiry body twisted restlessly in the chair, his pale blue eyes glowed with enthusiasm, and the flush of nervous excitement that spread across his freckled face clashed gloriously with his thinning carrot-red hair. "Did I tell you, Leslie? It's the most extraordinary thing I've ever seen! Why, this man makes the Gaynor twins look like amateurs! This could be the most important thing to happen to psi research in decades. And you've only seen a fraction of it. We've been testing him all week—the man is practically limitless. He can go into delta wave in less than thirty seconds and maintain it—well, as you've seen, almost indefinitely. It's incredible. Just incredible. This could be the breakthrough we've been waiting for."

Leslie said, "Hmm," and watched the man in the room opposite them, who was resting his head on his folded arms, looking for all appearances as though he were asleep. She was reluctant to dampen George's enthusiasm, so she gave him a quick smile before the doubt that was plain in her thoughts became evident on her face. A breakthrough they definitely needed, but she was not about to seize on this man as the answer to their prayers. Not yet.

"Vital signs back to normal," Malcolm announced

curtly, and then leaned back in his chair with a huge sigh that could have measured either relief or amazement. He took off his glasses and rubbed the bridge of his nose, shaking his head slowly. "I've never seen anything like it."

"Hmm," Leslie said again, and the skepticism in her tone was disguised by musing. "Almost too good to be true, isn't it?"

Both George and Malcolm directed sharp, questioning glances at her, but she missed them because at that moment Michael Bradshaw lifted his head. He looked relaxed, restored, goldenly beautiful. He turned toward the mirror, and for one disconcerting moment Leslie was certain that those peculiar yellow eyes were looking right at her. Of course the man would have to have been stupid not to realize that *someone* was behind the mirror, but there was absolutely no way he could have singled her out. Yes Leslie was certain that was precisely what he had done, an impression that was confirmed when his smoothly tanned face relaxed into a self-confident, wonderfully cocky smile—rather like a child who knows he has performed well and has every intention of rewarding himself for it. Never removing his eyes from her, he lifted his sweater-clad arms over his head, fingers linked together as he stretched the sinewy muscles of his arms and torso, and then, impudently, he winked at Leslie and got to his feet.

Malcolm hurried to the connecting door to release their prisoner from his volunteer confinement, and Leslie turned away quickly, her hand self-consciously going to her throat as she tried to convince herself that Michael Bradshaw couldn't possibly have seen her, and that what had just passed between them was *not* a personal exchange of the flirtatious variety.

"Well?" demanded George eagerly, swiveling his chair around to face her and leaving it spinning as he leaped up. "What did you think? You haven't said a word. It's fantastic, isn't it? Lord, Leslie, just imagine what we can learn from this guy. We've got years of research material in one man alone. Well?" he insisted. "What do you think?"

Leslie forced a laugh that was as noncommittal as it could possibly be without hurting George's feelings or challenging his professional judgment. "You're asking the wrong person, George. I'm a psychologist first, remember; parapsychology is just a sideline with me."

"Oh, pshaw!" retorted George good-naturedly. The energy that radiated from him was electric, and he looked excited enough to levitate. "You've devoted more time to this center in the past five years than any one of the rest of us, and a hell of a lot more than you've given any of your so-called respectable projects. Come on." Now he was wheedling. "All I'm asking for is a professional opinion."

Leslie smiled at him. Insecurity was a professional hazard, and George could hardly be blamed, given the circumstances, for begging for a little reassurance. But in all fairness, all she could reply was, "And I can hardly give you that until after I've interviewed him, can I?" But then, seeing how George's countenance fell, she relented. "What I saw," she added, carefully tempering honesty with gentleness, "was incredibly... impressive. Incredibly!"

And because Leslie didn't want to think about just *how* incredible what she had witnessed was, she was relieved when Malcolm opened the door of the small booth and informed her, "I've sent him on ahead to your office, Les." Then, with a quick wink and a grin, "Some show, huh?"

George opened his mouth, but before he could speak, Leslie raised a hand and promised him, "The minute I finish my report."

George had the grace to look abashed, though companionably so, as he turned to gather up his notes. Leslie, clutching her own blank notepad to her chest in what she hoped was not too blatantly defensive a gesture, left the small booth and made her way toward her office.

The Center for the Study of Psi and Related Phenomena had been established in 1952, two years before Leslie's birth, by her uncle, Albert Roarke. Even though some study upon the subject was already beginning to be conducted at Duke University, the research center was a risk, a bizarre deviation, and an embarrassment to the respectable scientific community from which Dr. Roarke had sprung. Leslie grew up in a family of physicians and scientists, and all her life she'd heard Uncle Albert referred to as the "black sheep," "the crazy old man," and, in tones of condescension that begged forgiveness for his eccentricity even while they offered no excuse, "the poor thing." Leslie was a teenager before she knew *what*, exactly, was the bizarre nature of Uncle Albert's life's work, so reluctant was the family to discuss him, and in the nature of the turbulent sixties and with her adolescent instinct for rebellion, she immediately championed his cause.

By the time she entered college, however, Leslie had swung full circle back to her family's conservative viewpoint, and consistently refused Uncle Albert's invitations to join him in field research. The Center was not quite the embarrassment to her that it had been to her parents, but she saw no reason to take it seriously and certainly had no intention of following in Uncle Albert's footsteps as an anathema to the spirit of scientific research.

Yet somewhere along the line Leslie had discovered within herself the same thirst for unanswered questions that had driven her Uncle Albert—the burning curiosity that many would say is the only true mark of a scientist—and she could not walk away from puzzles unsolved. At the Center for the Study of Psi and Related Phenomena there were unsolved puzzles in abundance.

After Uncle Albert died, Leslie began to volunteer her skills at the Center. Now she divided her time equally between the local hospital for disadvantaged children and the Center. Her parents—who had never recovered from their disappointment over the fact that she had chosen psychology, the bastard child of psychiatry, as her profession and, having made such a disastrous choice, she had not gone into private practice—had somehow managed to resign themselves to their daughter's betrayal by noting that she *was* performing a service of sorts, and that the people she saw at the Center were, for the most part, in desperate need of a good psychologist.

That, of course, was the crux of the matter. In the five years of her work at the Center the examples of unexplained phenomena Leslie had actually encountered could be counted on the fingers of one hand. For the most part the people who claimed supernatural powers or paranormal visitations were the victims of easily explained psychoses who benefitted greatly from Leslie's therapy. Even those cases she could not explain entirely did not disturb her; they were, she maintained, only examples of answers she had not found yet. And that, perhaps, was why this interview with Michael Bradshaw was making her so nervous. She had a very strong feeling this was one phenomenon that would not be so easy to explain away—and she could not be certain whether it was dread or excitement that was beating rapidly in her chest as she approached the door of her office.

Leslie paused a moment in the corridor, taking a deep breath, automatically straightening the collar of the crisp white lab coat that was a symbol of her professional status and smoothing down the crown of her sometimes fly-away blond hair. She caught herself in these instinctive grooming motions and grimaced, feeling foolish. She could hardly expect to get anywhere with Michael Bradshaw if she let him know he had intimidated her before they had even met, and honestly, he was no different from any of the dozens of others she had interviewed in similar situations.

Or not much.

She paused with her hand on the doorknob, thinking briefly and longingly about the smooth Caribbean sands and sparkling waters she had just left, and then she squared her shoulders determinedly, fixed a confident smile on her face, and pushed open the door. "Good morning, Mr. Bradshaw," she said in the general direction of the figure who was lounging comfortably on her sofa. "I'm Dr. Roarke, and I will be working with you for the rest of the day."

Chapter Two

Michael had been sipping contentedly from a large tumbler of iced orange juice, looking around the eclectically decorated little office and absently trying to imagine the woman to whom its distinctive stamp of personality belonged. Middle-aged, he had decided, perhaps even a grandmother, judging by the photographs on her desk. Plump and matronly and cheerfully bustling, the type of woman who brought homemade brownies to work to share with her colleagues and who did needlepoint between clients. Michael had resolved to enjoy the upcoming encounter to its fullest, for she also appeared to be a woman with an appreciable sense of humor.

He got to his feet when the door opened, and he was almost unable to conceal his surprise. *Young*, he thought with an unexpected prickle of irritation. *She's so young!*

But he extended his hand with a smile designed to charm the soulless and said, "I can't think of a better way to spend the afternoon."

Leslie took his hand in her cool, dry one and couldn't help but register the warmth and the vitality that seemed to surge from his handclasp. She retrieved her hand perhaps a little too quickly and knew precisely why the prospect of this interview had made her nervous. Michael Bradshaw was one of the most energetically attractive men she had ever met, and it was sensuality, not mysticism, that radiated from him like an aura. How in the world was she supposed to resign this incredibly physical man with the very unphysical things she had just seen him do?

Leslie moved behind her cluttered desk, busily pushing aside stacks of case files, two weeks' worth of accumulated mail and various other paper clutter, feeling those tawny eyes, relaxed, alert and friendly, upon her all the while. She said, "You'll have to forgive me for a moment while I get organized. I've been on vacation."

"So they told me." He waited a polite moment after she sat down and then resumed his seat on the sagging flower-print sofa. "Who are the children?" he asked curiously.

Leslie hesitated in the process of extracting her portable tape recorder from a drawer, and then realized he meant the photographs on her desk. "Oh, those. Some of my patients." At his questioning look she smiled, a little placatingly, and explained, "I also do family counseling and child psychology."

"Ah." He assumed an air of thoughtful wisdom, but the twinkling eyes gave him away. "I suppose one can only take so much of ghosts and wizards before it ceases to be a challenge."

Leslie's smile deepened, almost reluctantly, in appreciation of his natural humor. In her line of work it was a rare occurrence to meet someone who didn't take himself too seriously, and Michael Bradshaw...well, he was something else again. She said, "I hope you don't mind if I record this session."

Michael shrugged. "Not at all. It won't play back, though, nothing I say ever does. You'd better take notes just to be on the safe side."

Leslie glanced at him suspiciously, but he had such a shuttered, innately mischievous, and totally unreadable face that it was impossible to tell whether he was serious. The scientist in Leslie compelled her, however, to test the recorder, playing back the sound of her own voice until she was certain everything was working. She tried not to look too smug as she placed the machine on the corner of the desk nearest Michael and rewound the tape. "Everything seems to be in working order," she pronounced pleasantly.

Michael smiled at her sweetly.

She pressed the record button and settled back in her chair. "I want you to think of this as just a get-acquainted session. We'll talk in general for a while about your background, your goals, ambitions, that sort of thing. Just feel comfortable to say whatever you please."

"Sure," Michael agreed easily, and Leslie watched the graceful movement of his arm as he reached for his glass of juice. "Where shall we begin? My childhood? My dreams?" A definite spark of mischief in his eyes betrayed his implacable expression. "My sex life?"

Wonderful, thought Leslie dryly. *A flirt, on top of everything else.* The woman in her couldn't help reacting to his charm while the professional in her resented mightily the complications it provoked, and not for the first time in her life she wished the Center could afford the services of another part-time psychologist. Her first impression of Michael Bradshaw had been correct: she was in way over her head.

But none of that showed on her face as she replied politely, "I hardly think we need to delve that deeply into your psyche right now, Mr. Bradshaw. Why don't we begin with something a bit more pertinent?"

"But sex is pertinent, you know," he persuaded her blandly, sipping his juice. Once again, only the subtle twinkle in his eyes revealed that he was anything other than perfectly serious. "Haven't you ever read Freud?"

He felt guilty for teasing her, but she had caught him off guard and he couldn't, on such short notice, think of any other way to disguise the fact. They'd warned him that Dr. Leslie Roarke was one smart lady, but he hadn't expected her to be so cool. If she was in any way impressed by his previous display of psychic prowess she was far from showing it, but that didn't offend him as much as it challenged him, and he was far more intrigued by her than disturbed. He simply hadn't expected her to be so young, and so...well, female.

Leslie smiled distantly. "I have read Freud," she assured him. "At length. But I usually try to save his theories as a last resort. All I'd really like to do right now is get to know you a little better."

"I'm at your utter disposal," replied Michael grandly, and this time a quirk of his lips, as well as his eyes, betrayed his amusement.

Leslie pretended to ignore the implication. On her notepad she scribbled, "defensive, evasive, insecure..." She added to herself, but did not write, *and as sexy as a big-budget ad*. Then, repressing a sigh of irritation mingled with regret, she wondered why all the attractive men she met were either patients or those who *should* have been patients, and why it seemed to be the curse of her life to keep bumping into toads in Prince Charming's clothing. With a wry grimace she hoped Michael didn't notice, she reminded herself that she had hardly chosen the best profession in which to meet stable, well-adjusted men, and Michael Bradshaw could hardly be blamed for his own sex appeal.

She looked up at him, giving him a smile that was meant to put him at his ease—though she could not remember ever seeing a man who looked less in need of reassurance than the relaxed, self-confident, and innately powerful Michael Bradshaw—and she asked him, "When did you first begin to notice your extraordinary powers, Mr. Bradshaw?"

Michael, sipping his juice and watching her through partially shaded eyes, was trying to list all the reasons he did *not* find her attractive. She was too tall, for one thing—almost his height—and he preferred petite women. Her hair, a lovely shade of blond, was marred by dark roots, though he liked the way she wore it—without pretense or artifice, long and slightly wavy around her shoulders, pushed carelessly behind her ears to keep it from tickling her face, the full crown forming a slight shadow over her forehead. Her makeup was minimal: light blue shadow on her eyelids and pale pink gloss on her lips that set off the light tan she had no doubt acquired on vacation. She did not look like the type of woman who spent much time on her personal appearance, but he found himself admiring that rather than disdaining it. She was wearing a tailored pink blouse with only one button undone at the collar, and burgundy slacks beneath the officious white lab coat, and from what he could tell, she was small-busted, not strikingly slim but certainly not full-figured. No hips. Small thighs that seemed inappropriate for her height and body build. That wasn't very sexy: Michael despised the fitness craze that inspired women to ignore their own femininity in favor of the unisex idea of the perfect model, and he preferred the feminine form with a few more curves in it.

Her nails were bluntly trimmed and unpolished, her wrists delicately boned and adorned by a plain black-banded watch on one arm, a fragile gold chain on the other. Her fingers were long and graceful, and infinitely fascinating to watch. She *did* have magnificent hands. And her throat. Long and slender, distinctly fluted at the collarbone, an artful support that drew attention to a face that was both severe and vulnerable, studious and open, guarded yet possessed of an innate humor. It was a face that challenged him into wanting to see it wreathed with laughter, softened with affection, intent with passion.

Inwardly, Michael sighed. It was no use. He *did* find her attractive. He could not explain in logical terms why it was so, but he knew enough about magic to recognize it when he saw it, and the chemistry of sexual recognition had struck him full in the face the moment she walked into the room. The only question that remained now was what he was going to do about it.

He commented mildly, "They told me you were on the board of directors here."

She did not miss his deliberate change of subject, but pretended to ignore it. The first rule of psychology was to let the patient set the course and, even though Michael

Bradshaw was not precisely a patient, it was difficult to readjust her thinking for the special circumstances. "Does that bother you?"

So, she was determined to play the doctor. Michael flashed her a grin. "Not at all. It helps to know who I'm supposed to impress."

"Why do you feel it necessary to impress me, Mr. Bradshaw?"

"Because you're a beautiful woman, of course," he returned smoothly.

Leslie folded her hands on her desk and looked at him easily, taking her time to absorb all the details. He had crossed one sneakered foot over his ankle; rich cocoa jeans shaped his calves and thighs and blended into a body-hugging sweater of a light cotton woven in shades of brown and gray. The sleeves of the sweater were pushed up to reveal strong forearms lightly dusted with pale gold hair and hands that were quick and light. He was not a heavily muscled man, nor a largely built one, and again the image of a cat came to mind as she tried to categorize him. Lean strength, sinewy grace, coiled alertness. She followed the shape of his torso upward to where the neck of his sweater scooped low over the collarbone and she was intrigued for a moment by the shapely hollow there, the strong masculine throat at its most vulnerable point. She let her eyes move at a leisurely pace upward, to the sharp, narrow face with its intriguing inscrutability, the magnificent mane of multicolored hair, those other-worldly eyes shaped by lashes so light they were almost invisible. All of him, so sun-washed and healthy, so striking and extraordinary. *I could believe it*, she thought dimly, hardly willing to admit the knowledge to herself. *I could believe that this man is the real thing. Good Lord, if he told me he was from another planet, I think I wouldn't doubt it for a minute.*

She said, smiling, "And you're a very attractive man, Mr. Bradshaw, which you no doubt know. But that isn't relevant here, either. I appreciate the fact that you are volunteering your time to us, and I don't want to seem unreasonable, but you could make my job a lot easier if you would just cooperate a little.''

Not only beautiful, Michael acknowledged with a flicker of admiration, but bright, savvy, and talented when it came to handling "difficult" clients, which was certainly what he was doing his best to be. *How the hell*, he found himself wondering with unexpected annoyance, *did she get mixed up with a place like this?*

He suggested, "Do we have to do the Mr. Bradshaw—Dr. Roarke bit? Wouldn't it make our relationship easier if we were on a first-name basis?''

"Not necessarily.'' There was a flicker of warning behind her saccharine smile, but in fact she was warming to him—more than she had planned to, but certainly no more than was inevitable. Two weeks in the islands and the only men she had met had been fifty, fat and balding. First day back on the job and who should present himself for her professional evaluation but Adonis incarnate? *Sailing*, she thought a little wistfully. *I'll bet he likes sailing.* She said, "Perhaps we should get on with the task at hand and discuss the matter of names later.''

He grinned winningly. "I thought the patient was always right in your business. Isn't that something of a rule of thumb?''

"But you're not exactly a patient, though, are you?''

He sipped his juice, looking interested. "Then what am I?''

Leslie was imagining Michael Bradshaw on the stern of a small, brightly colored boat, wearing tight white shorts and deck shoes, the wind billowing his nylon jacket away from his naked chest and ruffling his hair, his eyes squinting into the sun, his strong hands grasping the lines as sea spray misted his legs....

She said, focusing back on the moment with difficulty, "I'm not sure I know what you mean. Didn't Dr. Jorgenson or Dr. Davis explain to you—''

"Yes, yes.'' He gave an impatient turn of his wrist. "I know all about the tests you do here and I've taken most of them. What I want to know is what I'm supposed to do with you." Quite disarmingly, he tilted his head with an explicit but nonetheless entrancing upward twist of his lips. "Now that you've eliminated the obvious, of course."

Leslie had to bow her head to disguise an unpreventable flirtatious response of her own lips. On her notepad she scribbled the word "incorrigible" and underlined it twice, liking the way it looked. That seemed to summarize most accurately all she knew of Michael Bradshaw so far, and she liked things that could be labeled.

In a moment she looked up, once again cool and smiling and distantly in control, and she said, "This is not a test, Michael." His first name slipped out without her being prepared for it, and the slight flicker of smug approval in his expression told her he had not missed it. She was annoyed with herself, and her tone became a little firmer. "Psychological evaluation is part of our research on every subject who comes through the Center." And that was even worse—referring to him as a "subject." Sometimes she hated this part of the work. "If there is a connection between psi or paranormal phenomena and the human brain, we intend to find it. For that reason your cooperation in this part of our study will be very much appreciated, although of course we'll understand if you don't feel comfortable undergoing the full psychological profile."

He looked at her curiously. "Do you really think that just by talking to me you'll be able to explain how I'm able to do the things I do?"

Her eyes were wide, and clear, and hazel, showing not the tiniest flicker of a doubt. "That, plus the results of the other tests you've taken and your EEGs—none of them alone can tell us much of anything, but the whole picture should be able to bring us at least one step closer to understanding whatever psychic phenomena are manifesting themselves through you."

Damn, Michael thought, and hid his irritation by bringing his glass once again to his lips. *She is really into this thing.* Why should that disappoint him so? It was all part of the game, and he had been told from the beginning that getting past Dr. Leslie Roarke was a primary part of the test. He would cooperate, because he had to, but his heart just wasn't in it anymore.

Leslie said patiently, folding her hands once again on top of her desk and leaning forward as though to encourage him in confidence, "Shall we return to my original question?"

"Which was?"

His gaze, Leslie noticed, had strayed to her breasts. It was an instinctive thing men did, as old as the handshake, completely involuntary and signifying nothing. Under other circumstances Leslie would have ignored it, but there was something about Michael Bradshaw that made such a gesture impossible to ignore, that made her not in the least desirous of ignoring it. She felt, in fact, another ancient and instinctive response begin in her with the motion of his eyes: a tingling of the skin, a dilating of the pupils, a subconscious invitation she was powerless to control. And he, being male—or perhaps simply being who he was—noticed the response and seized it immediately.

His eyes met hers, gently gleaming with that purely sensual mixture of knowledge and challenge, and his voice dropped a fraction in timbre as he suggested, "Are you sure you wouldn't rather talk about my sex life? It's much more interesting, I promise you."

Leslie held his gaze, returned his smile, and maintained her composure. "I would rather," she informed him without compromise, "talk about when you first discovered your telekinetic powers."

There was a shadow of something in his eyes that was gone too quickly for her to define—irritation, or simple disappointment—and then he shrugged and got to his feet, wandering over to the window. "When I was about twelve, I suppose." His tone was disinterested, and he stood with his back to her, looking out over the tangled garden below. "Nothing dramatic at first, tipping domino houses and making pencils roll off desks, things like that. It got better as I practiced. You really should hire a gardener for this place. That could be a beautiful little spot down there if it had a little attention."

"We can't afford one." On her notepad Leslie jotted, "Onset of telekinesis with puberty, check parallels." Then, almost as a method of revenge for his merciless flirtation earlier, which had come very close to rattling her, she wrote, "Sexually motivated? Or sexually insecure? Sexual aggressiveness possibly sign of internalization..."

"Well, if I were you," Michael said, without turning, "when that grant comes through, I'd allocate a little money up front to sprucing up the place. Appearances mean a lot, you know."

Leslie looked up from her notepad and frowned, wondering who had told him about their application for government aid. Whoever it was had no right discussing institute business with an outsider, and she intended to look into the matter without further delay. She was just about to question him about it when he turned lazily from the window, hands in pockets, regarding her with subtle amusement lurking behind the unreadable planes of his face.

"By the way," he added carelessly, "I'm not insecure, and I'm not internalizing. What I am doing, my dear Dr. Roarke, is making a not-so-subtle pass at you. I'm surprised you didn't notice earlier."

For just a moment Leslie was nonplussed. There was no way he could have seen what she was writing from that angle, and his back had been to her the entire time. *Circumstantial*, she assured herself, a little weakly. *Sheerly circumstantial evidence.* Besides, it wasn't her job to make judgments about the validity or invalidity of a subject's skills; she merely collected data to be reviewed later by the entire committee. It was just that, standing there by the window, with the dusky morning sun forming a yellow-white aura around his body and bouncing off his hair and casting his face into shadows... It was just that, looking for a moment into those incredible eyes, she could almost believe...anything.

But she would not let him guess that. For some reason, it was very important to her not to let him know just how close she was to believing in him. So she said, very unprofessionally, the first thing that came into her mind. "Why would you want to do that?"

He came over to her, his movements so sinuous and silent that she was hardly aware that he had moved at all until he was directly before her, his hands braced upon her desk, leaning down until his golden-brown face was almost on a level with hers and his eyes, like muted sunlight, filled her vision. Dimly she was aware of the fragrance of his cologne, something indefinable and vaguely exotic, yet with a sharp underbite, like the first taste of curry to an unaccustomed palate. Smooth yet sharp, like the man himself.

He said, very softly, "More to the point, why would I not?"

How strange. Until this moment, Leslie had not given much thought to how unaccustomed she was to receiving overt, genuine passes from men, especially from the type of man to whom she might like to respond. Now she realized that it was such a rare occurrence she hardly knew how to react, and she had to be doubly careful not to be swept away by the novelty of it all.

For it would be very, very easy to be swept away by a man like Michael Bradshaw.

She realized that the strange warmth she was feeling was an unexpected flush in her skin, and that her pulse had accelerated imperceptibly with his closeness. Even her breathing had unconsciously begun to synchronize with the gentle rise and fall of his, for he was so near she imagined she could feel its flutter on her cheek. She realized, with no small surprise, that she was falling under what is commonly known as a spell.

Quickly, almost with a snap, she brought herself back to the matter at hand. Missing hardly more than a beat, she inquired, "How does it make you feel, to be able to do things—to control things—that other people cannot?"

Michael straightened up with a lazy smile, accepting defeat gracefully. *God*, he thought, *she is smooth*. As little respect as he had for psychologists in general, he had to admit he was impressed by this one. He imagined she would be a great asset to her field. But then what in the world was she doing in a place like this?

"Well," he answered her question, "I'll tell you one thing. I'm never bored."

"Umm." Leslie glanced down at her notepad, but didn't write anything. Her heart was still beating a little erratically from their close encounter of a moment before. "I imagine not."

He cocked his head curiously, and his next comment seemed motivated out of a genuine desire to know. "You're not used to it, are you? Men coming on to you, I mean. Why is that?"

Leslie decided, for the moment, that it was much easier not to try to fight the inevitable. He was in control of the conversation just as, if the truth be told, he had always been. With a small sigh, she leaned back in her chair and returned his open gaze. "I'm not exactly the singles-bar type, Mr. Bradshaw. My work keeps me so busy that there's very little time left over for—social amenities."

He appeared to consider this. "No steady boyfriend, then? You've never been married?"

Her smile became a little rueful, but she tried to dismiss it with a shrug. "Most men back off when they discover what line of work I'm in. They tend to expect me to be constantly analyzing them, I suppose, or they're afraid I'll rate their performance in bed and prescribe therapy." She laughed a little self-consciously, acutely aware of how easily the conversation had slipped to a personal basis, and how quickly. "In other words, I seem to make men uncomfortable in social situations."

Michael's eyes were twinkling. "Only very insecure men," he pointed out. "And as I've already clarified, that is not one of my problems. I have absolutely no fear of being rated on performance in bed—and besides, I take instruction very well.''

Leslie choked on a laugh. *Outrageous*, she thought, and picked up her pen to write it down, but quickly thought better of it. Making those harmless little notes to herself was one habit she was obviously going to have to overcome now that she had discovered Michael Bradshaw could apparently see through walls. And anyway, she had thought of a better adjective for him. *Delightful.*

Delighted was exactly what he looked as he regarded her, matching the laughter in her eyes with warmth in his own. She thought irrelevantly what a fun date he would be, despite his rather unusual talents and his undeniable closetful of psychoses and neuroses just waiting to be discovered. And it was with a regretful inner sigh that she reminded herself sternly of the purpose of their meeting. Why couldn't any of the men she met ever be normal?

She said, ''Now, I think I've done my fair share of contributing to the spirit of the interview. Do you think we could talk about you for a while?''

But he, apparently, did not. Hardly even regarding her suggestion, he inquired, ''How did you get interested in this sort of research, anyway?''

''My uncle founded the Center,'' she informed him, absently checking the amount of tape left on the spool.

Michael frowned. She really *was* in deep, and he was annoyed with himself that it mattered. After all, none of that made her any less attractive—just slightly less of a challenge. ''Sort of a family heritage, hmm?'' he pursued, wanting to draw her out.

''Sort of.'' It was becoming apparent that she was going to have to let him set the pace, and Leslie tried to be patient. Obviously, this was taking longer than planned, and she'd hoped to have a full report ready for the committee meeting at noon. Oh, well, she couldn't be held responsible for uncooperative subjects, and she would simply have to do the best she could.

Michael wandered for a moment around the perimeters

of the small room that, with its fading calico wallpaper and multitude of knickknacks, resembled a cozy country kitchen more than a professional office. The furniture was garage-sale special, the walls adorned with crayon scribblings and watercolors of her former patients, the curtains bleached white priscillas trimmed with patterned ruffles vaguely resembling the antique periwinkle blue of the wallpaper. The room was bright, warm, and welcoming; the good things that emanated from it had been like a cheerful greeting the first moment Michael walked in. He wondered what Leslie's home looked like, and if he would ever find out.

Leslie had been watching him move, not with the observant detachment of a clinician, who might have noticed restlessness, uneasiness, concealed stress, and duly written it all down on her ever-ready notepad, but with the simple pleasure of one watching something that was graceful, natural and easy to observe, a dancer, perhaps, or a forest creature in its own habitat. She wasn't surprised when he stopped before her, nor did she allow herself to be distracted by his next question.

"Does it bother you," he asked, and there was nothing on his face but idle curiosity, "that I can do these supernatural things?"

If he had expected a flip or placating reply, he was to be disappointed. In fact, Leslie knew that she should have turned the question back on him—it was *his* feelings she was interested in, after all—but somehow she felt their relationship had already gone beyond such games. So she gave due and careful consideration to her reply.

"If you mean," she answered after a moment, "am I impressed with your—powers..." She smiled a little and shrugged, almost in apology. "I have to tell you, Mr. Bradshaw, that I don't believe in miracles, nor do I acknowledge the supernatural, in the accepted sense of the word. You are able to do things most of us can't, but all I'm really interested in is why. So I suppose the answer to your question is no, it doesn't bother me. What *does* bother me, however—'' for now she had to get firm ''—is that I have a meeting in less than twenty minutes and we haven't even begun this interview. Now I really have just a few basic questions I have to ask you. Do you think we could postpone this conversation until after I've finished?''

Now Michael was really confused. She didn't believe in the supernatural, did she? She sat there, looking so earnest and so vulnerable and so damned approachable. He was half inclined to call the whole thing off, right then. He was much more interested in what was going on inside the head of Dr. Leslie Roarke than he was in what was going on behind the walls of the Center for the Research of Psi and Related Phenomena. But then he was irritated again, and guilty. No, he had a job to do. This was important; it was every bit as important to him as it was to her, though for vastly different reasons. And he was going to see it through.

But he dreaded the moment of reconciliation with Dr. Leslie Roarke.

Michael smiled, dazzlingly, and spread his hands in an open gesture of apology. ''I have a short attention span,'' he explained. ''I guess I should have warned you. Okay, I'm ready; let's get to work. I'm great on Rorschach. How about a little free association? I also read minds and do great card tricks, you know.''

Leslie laughed lightly, helplessly, liking him more and more. ''I know,'' she responded somewhat dryly, and motioned him to be seated. ''But we're not going to tackle anything quite so difficult this morning. If you'll just—''

Her telephone rang.

''Leslie.'' Malcolm's voice was apologetic. ''I know your time isn't up yet, but could you let me borrow him for a few minutes? There're some test results I really should check before the meeting. You know I wouldn't do this to you if it wasn't important.''

Leslie glanced at her watch and swore silently. To Malcolm she said, ''No problem. I've gotten just about all I can here, anyway.'' What she had gotten was nothing, but she had the distinct impression that she could spend the rest of the day with the evasive and desperately charming Michael Bradshaw and be no farther ahead in her assessment than she was now. Malcolm could hardly do worse. "I'll send him along to your office right now."

"Thanks, Leslie." A pause, then his curiosity overcome him. "What do you think?"

Leslie's lips tightened into something halfway between a grimace and a self-mocking smile. "Not much," was all she replied, and hung up the phone.

Michael was already on his feet. "I feel like everybody's favorite toy," he commented on his way to the door, but with an easygoing display of resignation. "Too bad, too." He paused to wink at her. "We were just getting to the good part."

Leslie, feeling a bit redundant and quite foolish, nonetheless felt compelled to inquire, "Don't you want to know where you're going?"

He looked at her patiently. "To Dr. Jorgenson's office, one flight up, second door on the right."

Of course. She should have known.

He opened the door, and then turned back to her. He looked at her for a moment thoughtfully. "How do you think I do it?" There was nothing in his voice but a genuine interest in her opinion.

"I haven't the faintest idea," she returned evenly. "How do *you* think you do it?"

He considered that for a moment, then replied with a quick and totally disarming wink, "Magic."

Leslie looked at him steadily. "I don't believe in magic, Mr. Bradshaw."

His return gaze was thoughtful and enigmatic. "What a pity," he replied after a moment. "Magic is the only thing I *do* believe in."

He stepped through the door and closed it behind him, but the smile he gave her on parting lingered long after he was gone.

With a sigh, Leslie rewound the tape and prepared to transcribe her notes. Not that there was anything useful to

transcribe. Forty-five minutes with the most exciting research subject to pass through the doors of the Center in
decades, and all she had to show for her time was an innocent flirtation recorded on tape. That was hardly likely
to go over well with the committee, and she decided to
erase the recording after she had finished listening to it.
There was no point in having that nonsense on file.

But as it turned out, there was no need to erase anything.
She pressed the play button, and waited...and waited. The
machine, which had been in perfect operating condition
when she had started out, had apparently malfunctioned
somewhere along the way. The tape of their interview was,
as Michael Bradshaw had predicted, completely blank.

Leslie spent a very long time staring thoughtfully at the
door through which Michael had left, listening to the cassette spin out its mysterious silence.

Chapter Three

Leslie had been opposed to the idea of applying for a government grant from the beginning. Besides her instinctive reluctance to become entangled with the red tape of federal bureaucracy, there was a very pertinent ethical question involved, and that ethical issue had yet to be resolved among the members of the board.

It was a little-known fact that the federal government invested millions of dollars each year in psychic research. That in itself was not a fact that inspired Leslie to suspicion—the purpose of research, after all, was to explore *all* areas of the unknown, and the untapped abilities of the human mind seemed as logical a place in which to invest funding as, say, the mating habits of a South American fruit fly. What bothered Leslie was the implied goal behind the government's generosity: psychic weaponry. Other countries, it was claimed, were already beginning to make headway in this field and it was only logical that the strongest branch of the government, the military, should supply the funding necessary to match their international adversaries' progress in what could very possibly prove to be the most important frontier of human endeavor.

It was the same issue that had plagued scientists from the beginning of time: any discovery, no matter how innocuous, had the potential to be put to destructive use. Leslie, rational as she was, realized that it was highly unlikely that anything would be discovered in their field of research with the potential to interest the military—at least, not in her lifetime—but the uneasy moral debate remained. It just felt to her, somehow, too much like selling out.

But it was also plainly obvious that the Center could not continue to do any kind of meaningful work without additional funding. Their sponsorship from universities was growing more inadequate every year, and private endowments could hardly be expected to pick up the slack. Expenses were rising, sophisticated tracking and recording equipment was desperately needed, and important field projects were more and more often ignored because they simply could not afford to send a crew and equipment out of the Center for the length of time necessary to prepare adequate reports. It was obvious something had to be done, and government funding seemed the only way.

For the past six months they had been hounded by inspectors and deluged by paperwork. More than once Leslie had declared it simply wasn't worth it. She was sick of trying to explain to nonscientists the strict scientific methods they used in recording and delineating their research. She was bone-weary of seeing expectation turn to disappointment on the faces of those who came to the Center expecting the Hollywood version of the supernatural—complete with flashing lights and floating ectoplasm—and discovered instead white mice and data graphs. She was tired of trying to impress people who refused to be impressed in order to receive something she wasn't at all certain she wanted, and by the time she had left on vacation she was half hoping that their application would be turned down and life could get back to normal—or seminormal—at the Center.

That, however, was apparently not to be the case. The memo on her desk that had greeted her this morning informed her that the agenda of the administrative board meeting at noon today would include a progress report of the status of their application for funds, as well as a review of "recent research in progress that might be pertinent to said application." In other words, Michael Bradshaw.

It was a few minutes before noon when Leslie shrugged out of her lab coat and grabbed her notepad with its few irrelevant scrawls. The business about the tape recorder was still bothering her—and had been bothering her since Michael had left the office. Magic, he had said. Was it possible that after all this time she had actually had an encounter with something—someone—totally inexplicable? And if so, what could it mean to the future of the Center? And more importantly, what would it mean to Leslie's own carefully regimented views on the subject of paranormal phenomena?

There were worse fates, she supposed, than to spend the rest of her life studying a man like Michael Bradshaw.

Before leaving her office, and with a harried glance at her watch, she picked up the telephone to call the Children's Hospital. All her patients had been stable before she'd left and she'd made no appointments for her first day back, but she wanted to be certain nothing had developed in her absence that required her attention.

"No major problems," reported Leslie's secretary after welcoming her back and enviously inquiring after the state of the Bahamas. That was one of the things Leslie preferred about the children's hospital over the research center: the luxury of a full-time, dutifully devoted, hospital-salaried secretary. "Dr. Pinchon wants to consult on one of his hearing-impaired patients, I've set up an appointment for Wednesday." Leslie made a note on her calendar. "Mrs. Griffin called a couple of times about Amy. She's started wetting the bed again." Leslie made an appropriate sound of sympathy but she wasn't really surprised. Amy had been scheduled for a visit with her father last weekend and those occasions were always traumatic. "Oh, and your father called..." There was a silence while Carol flipped through messages. "Six times. He seemed very annoyed you weren't here, but he didn't want to call you at the hotel. He claimed it wasn't urgent."

Leslie's father didn't believe in answering machines, so there had been no message for her at home when she'd arrived. And because he utterly refused to acknowledge that she worked at the Center, he naturally had continued to harass Carol at the hospital rather than leaving a message for her here. And just as typically, he had not left a real message; he simply expected Leslie to call him back when she got a chance.

"Six times, hmm?" Leslie absently made a note on her calendar to return the calls. "Sounds pretty urgent to me." Her curiosity was mildly aroused, but she was not going to make returning that phone call a top priority. Encounters with her family were never very pleasant, and she avoided them as often as she could.

"I'll try to come by the hospital sometime this afternoon," she told Carol, "but it sounds as if things are pretty quiet over there." Contrary, she thought with a grimace at her watch, to what they were over here. "If you don't hear from me again today I'll be in first thing tomorrow morning, and you can reach me either at the Center or at home."

"Sure thing," Carol responded brightly. "I'll hold down the fort until then."

Leslie spared herself a brief smile as she hung up the phone. If one thing in this world could be counted on, it was that Carol would hold down the fort. She was so efficient that at times she made Leslie feel positively redundant.

She was five minutes late for the meeting by the time she hurried across the sun-speckled lawn toward the administrative building. Punctuality had never been one of Leslie's compulsions, but she wondered if tardiness on this occasion was no more than an evasion tactic. She had never been so unprepared for a meeting, and despite her self-imposed restrictions upon making judgments, she knew she would be expected to render an opinion on Michael Bradshaw. What could she say except he was a puzzle, an enigma, a complete bafflement...? That secrets were no longer secrets when Michael was around, that he could read written messages without seeing them and hear telephone conversations without hearing them and that tape recorders didn't work in his presence.... That level-headed, reasonable, basically skeptical Dr. Leslie Roarke was for the first time utterly confounded and more than a little captivated by the wizard who wore the guise of Michael Bradshaw.

They were gathered impatiently in the administration office—George, Malcolm and Winston Monroe, the Center's hired administrator and the only nonscientist of the group. Styrofoam cups of coffee and half-empty cellophane bags of chips littered the coffee table and the corner of Winston's desk, for even at their most formal this group were not high on decorum—a characteristic that Winston, a born bureaucrat despite the unorthodox nature of his work, had never learned to get used to.

Like Leslie's office, Winston's was small, multi-windowed and cheaply furnished. But there the similarity ended. The walls were covered with an inexpensive, though tasteful, wood paneling that added dignity to the surroundings; the hardwood floor was covered by pale gray nylon carpeting. The sofa on which George and Malcolm rather nervously perched was black Naugahyde, and matching sling chairs were drawn up on either side of the polished oak-veneer desk. The only marks of personality were the framed diplomas on the wall and a five-by-seven photograph on the center of his usually spotless desk of Winston's wife and child. As Leslie rushed in Winston looked up, frowning, brushing crumbs off his desk, and announced, "I thought you'd forgotten!"

"No," replied Leslie a little breathlessly. "Just got held up." She sank into one of the sling chairs and crossed her legs, trying to look composed while improvising a semiprofessional report. "I'm afraid I wasn't able to get very far with Mr. Bradshaw," she began by way of apology to Malcolm and George. "We're going to have to schedule another session this afternoon. But it's probably just as well. I'd like to hear the results of your reports first."

Malcolm and George looked somewhat disappointed, for

teamwork was the essence of success in research such as theirs, but Winston dismissed it. "That's not important," he said, his smooth, round face managing somehow to look both earnest and eager behind officious wire-rimmed glasses. "What I'd like from all of you now is a consensus: are the three of you convinced that this man is the genuine article?"

There was only the slightest hesitation, a few glances, and then Malcolm and George nodded. "Without a doubt," said George.

"According to every test we were able to devise," agreed Malcolm, "this man has demonstrated a capacity for psi phenomena unlike anything that has ever been seriously studied before."

Winston's gaze fell, questioning, on Leslie. She could not avoid an answer. "His abilities are...extraordinary," she agreed carefully. "I do believe his case bears further investigation."

Winston, satisfied, gave a curt nod and got to his feet. "Good," he said. "Then we're ready to begin."

He walked over to the door and opened it. Michael Bradshaw, smiling, walked in.

The three scientists looked in some surprise at one another, for it certainly was not customary to invite the subject of their research to a meeting at which his case was being discussed. Leslie opened her mouth to protest, but Winston, looking a great deal like the cat who had swallowed the canary, did not give her a chance.

"Doctors," he declared with a flourish, "may I present Michael Bradshaw...the best magician in the country today."

LESLIE'S FIRST THOUGHT WAS, *Impossible!* Then grimly, *Damn it, I knew it. I knew he was too good to be true.* And then outrage, fury and a sense of betrayal she was unable to justify even to herself took over and she was incapable of thinking anything coherent at all.

Malcolm said quietly, "What the hell...?"

And George, his pale eyes looking enormous in a suddenly sallow face, murmured, "I'm not sure I understand...."

Winston nodded smugly to both of them. "Precisely my point. He fooled you all, got past your state-of-the-art high-tech equipment, and even—" now he flashed a triumphant glance toward Leslie "—convinced our oh-so-cautious Dr. Roarke. Pretty impressive, doctors, you have to admit. Or pretty frightening, depending on how you want to look at it."

There was an outcry from the other two men, angry and defensive protestations of, "What is the meaning of this?" "This is an outrage, Winston, we won't stand for it." But Leslie didn't trust herself to speak. She was fuming; she could feel the heat in her cheeks and the sting of bitten-back indignation in her throat, and when she met Michael's eyes, that didn't help at all. Amusement was evident in those preternatural, inhuman-colored eyes, and something that looked like puzzlement, perhaps even an apology. Leslie quickly jerked her own gaze away. *Those damn eyes*, she thought furiously. *That's what convinced me. If it hadn't been for those ridiculous yellow eyes...*

But she knew that wasn't it at all. The fact was, she had believed him because for the first time in her life she had wanted to, and in wanting to she had broken her own cardinal rule and made herself vulnerable to suggestibility. Or perhaps simply vulnerable.

"Gentlemen." Michael's voice broke calmly through the uproar. With a slight lift of his hand he seemed to compel them to silence, but the looks that George and Malcolm directed toward him were suspicious, hostile and very disgruntled. Still they allowed him the courtesy to speak. "I apologize for the deception, but I assure you it was necessary. I can only ask you to take my word that it was not meant with malice or an intent to waste your time." His lips softened with a hint of his most endearing smile, one that surprisingly did a great deal to placate the bristling scientists. They settled back in their chairs and looked prepared to listen to Michael's story.

Winston resumed his seat behind his desk and Michael crossed the room easily, his voice calm and authoritative. He did not look at Leslie again. "In the past few days," he said, "I have duplicated every example of psychic phenomena you have ever studied at this clinic, and even shown you a few things you're not likely to see again." He paused a moment before arranging himself in the chair across from Leslie, his expression firm and fixed. "Each one of them," he said deliberately, "was an illusion. And most of them can be performed by any apprentice magician. The point being—" and he sank lazily into the chair, smiling ingeniously "—that it takes a liar to recognize a liar. I had to prove that to you before we could go any further."

Leslie was struck by how different he seemed now than he had been in her office. There he had been charming, open, playful and painfully easy to like. Here he was authoritative, confident and precise. A man who was accustomed to being in control and saw no reason for ingratiating games. He was apparently possessed of as many chimeric personalities as dazzling tricks, which Leslie supposed would be only standard fare for a master magician. And then she had to repeat the word to herself again, incredulously. *Magician.*

She thought his own description of himself was more apropos. *Liar.*

Winston spoke into the brief silence, obviously anxious to forestall any more accusations or questions until he had explained himself fully. "You've got to understand, doctors, that in research such as ours fraud is one of the biggest concerns, not only for us but for our sponsors."

"Damn it, Winston, you know that's not fair!" Malcolm could apparently contain himself no longer. "We run a first-class shop here—"

"Our methods are inarguable," George said defensively, agitated. "Every detail is subjected to the closest scientific scrutiny. It takes years to complete a single case file and we never release any data unless its been proven by the tightest scientific methods. You know that, Winston. It's you who are always complaining it takes too long to get results—''

"If we wanted to go for the quick kill we *would* release reports prematurely," Malcolm cut in angrily. "But our standards are too high for even that. Now you have the audacity to accuse us of fraud...."

Winston, sensing he was losing control of the situation, looked distracted, but again Michael calmed the melee with the quiet assertion in his voice. "I took the liberty," he said, "of glancing through some of your case files for the past few years." His voice was thoughtful, his expression blank. "Psychosurgery—it's a technique often used by Indian shamans to impress their tribesmen and keep the disrespectful in line, using cotton balls and chicken blood. I notice that your 'surgeon' in that case conveniently disappeared when you made arrangements for him to come into the Center and perform his techniques on lab animals— animals are much harder to hypnotize, you know, than humans. You had a wonderfully documented case of a young man who consistently scored nine out of ten by reading the order in which cards were displayed from a random deck. Professional gamblers—and magicians—use the same system to make their living, they just don't talk about it. And the young woman who could project images onto a blank television screen? I'm embarrassed to say it—'' and he swept them with a half-amused glance ''—it's all done with mirrors." He shrugged. "I could go on."

Leslie clenched her fists and felt her teeth lock tightly together. *All right, Winston, have your say, because then I've got something to say.*

Winston, as though sensing her thoughts and the impending storm, deliberately did not glance her way and hurried to explain, "The point is, even the most careful scientific tracking is subject to error without an expert on the scene, especially in a field as—'' he paused delicately ''—untried as this." Then, quickly, "You *know* I'm proud of the work we do here—even though I'm not a scientist I think of this place as my own and it's a reflection on *my* pride, too, that we've always been above reproach. I've always done the best for the Center, haven't I? And I've always had the best for the scientific community at large in mind...."

An exaggeration, perhaps, but Malcolm seemed to be willing to forgive Winston that in order to approach the more pertinent question. "Then why are you questioning us now?" he demanded. "Why bring in this-this—" He gestured toward Michael, his color rising, and Leslie thought for an absurd moment that he was going to give way to theatrics and declare Michael a viper in their bosom or a wolf in their flock. He controlled himself, however, and finished with a flourish: "This *charlatan*, in order to expose something that simply isn't here?"

Winston released a long-suffering sigh. "That's just the point, Malcolm. It wasn't my idea. I *know* what we do here, and how well it's done. But the government, you see, has to be a bit more careful with funds. Their position with the public on funding this kind of research is tenuous at best, and they can't afford even a breath of a scandal. They have chosen us as something of a test project and if we fail... Well, the whole program could go down the tubes. So they insist upon some sort of fail-safe device. And Michael Bradshaw," he finished simply, "is it."

I will never, Leslie thought in dim amazement, *understand the workings of the bureaucratic mind. They're nervous about funding psychic research, so they send in a magician to guard against fraud.* She was certain there was a thread of logic in there somewhere, but it had to be the kind of rationale that would only appeal to another bureaucrat...such as Winston.

At last, Leslie spoke up. "Then Mr. Bradshaw will be joining our staff?"

Winston had jumped a little at the sound of her voice, but looked relieved when her question was such an innocuous one. Obviously he had expected that, after her long and contained silence, she would be building up to a tirade, which of course she was; Leslie simply expressed herself with less volatility than George or Malcolm.

"Well, no," Winston said. "Not permanently, that is. You see, Michael has a full-time teaching position at Georgetown University. He'll only be here in an advisory capacity for the summer."

"In other words just long enough to fulfill the conditions of the grant." Leslie's voice was cool.

"I wish you people would at least try to be reasonable about this," Winston said plaintively. "If you would think about it for only a minute you'd see that this is going to benefit the Center's overall productivity as well as its reputation. It's *not* just the money, though God knows we're grateful for that." He directed at them a wide-scan glare that defied any of them to dispute. Then he continued persuasively. "Michael, while he's here, will be helping to refine your investigative techniques; he'll be cutting your research time in half, teaching you things you couldn't possibly learn on your own. This is a chance for us to make strides in the field we wouldn't have dreamed of ten years ago—and it's also a chance for us to prove to the world at large that psychic research is a valid scientific endeavor with controlled research methods and provable results. What can you possibly object to in that?"

He had a point, and Malcolm and George acknowledged it with an uneasy silence. Leslie, however, was more thoughtful. She could feel Michael's gaze upon her, but she did not return it. "I have one objection," she said at last, and she looked directly at Winston. "Between the three of us..." She nodded curtly in the direction of Malcolm and George. "We have almost seventy years of education and experience in our specialized fields. Yet we're supposed to take the word of this...layman concerning whether or not our research and conclusions are valid." Now she met Michael's gaze, her own stony. "You said it *could* be done with mirrors," she pointed out. "Can you actually prove that it *was*?"

Malcolm and George shot her a look of triumphant agreement; Winston looked flustered. Michael simply looked at her calmly, expressionlessly, and apparently intended to make no reply at all.

"Of course he can't prove it after the fact," Winston inserted huffily, losing patience. "That's not the point—"

"The point," interrupted Leslie coolly, never once faltering under Michael's admittedly unnerving gaze, "is that there is no doubt in my mind that everything we investigate here can be explained away if one tries hard enough. After all, that's what skeptics have been doing for years, and that's why, presumably, the Center was established—to investigate *all* explanations. But if we're going to take the first explanation that comes along..." A lift of her shoulders was simple and eloquent. "Then it seems to me our work here is ended. We could all make a lot more money— and get a lot more recognition for our work—if we went into more accepted forms of research and left the Center to the magicians, now couldn't we?"

Winston, for the moment, was nonplussed, and it was Michael who was at last forced to address her. "I'm not after your job, Dr. Roarke," he said mildly, and still she could read nothing in his face or his eyes. All she saw was a man who was very much in control and ultimately certain of himself. That alone would have been enough to intimidate a lesser woman. "I am, in fact, trying to make it easier. Yes, while I'm here I'm going to do my best to expose the people who come here. But I won't be doing any hasty guesswork, and I'm not asking you to take my word for anything. If I can prove to you beyond a shadow of a doubt—and it's my job to do so—that your research is invalid or that one of your subjects is a fraud, then I've saved you time and effort and saved the clinic embarrassment. But if *I* can't explain what I see..." He sounded highly doubtful that such an event would ever occur, but he concluded with a shrug. "Well, then, you'll know that what you're investigating is a genuine paranormal phenomenon, and you'll know exactly where to place your priorities."

Winston nodded enthusiastically. "Precisely! Don't you see this can only be the best for everyone?" But he didn't wait for an answer, and looked as though he was eager to end the meeting while a truce was still a tenuous possibility and before a full-scale riot broke out. "Now," he continued briskly, "I know you're all professionals and you'll be quick to cooperate with Michael and give him whatever help he needs." He turned to Michael. "Why don't you take the rest of the week to get oriented, know your way around, and catch up on our current projects? Leslie will be your liaison; she has access to all the information you'll need. For now…" He stood, a signal for the others to do the same. Leslie remained seated. "Let's be grateful for what we have. This funding is going to solve a lot of problems around here."

And create a lot more, was the unspoken consensus among the three scientists, but no one said anything as they filed toward the door. Malcolm and George, obviously anticipating a private meeting, glanced anxiously in Leslie's direction, but she made no move to follow them. Michael, bringing up the rear, closed the door behind him without looking at her once.

When the two of them were alone, Winston released a resigned sigh and resumed his seat behind his desk. Leslie, perhaps due to respect for her name, perhaps simply through the thrust of her personality, carried more authority than any of the other staff members, and Winston knew that in the final accounting it was she he would have to deal with. Not that she was generally unreasonable; they clashed frequently on matters pertaining to budget and efficiency, but both of them realized that Winston was never more concerned with anything other than the well-being of the Center, and that he was, when all was said and done, the only man for the job.

Yes, they had had their disagreements, but Leslie knew that, if push came to shove, Winston would have gladly emptied his own bank account to serve the Center and she had never seriously had cause to question his judgment before. She knew they were up against a wall on this matter of funding; she knew Winston had made the only possible choice, concessions notwithstanding. And it was for this reason that she thought very carefully before speaking.

Winston watched her warily from behind the desk. He was surprised when she looked up, very calmly, and said only, "I've never heard of him."

Winston looked puzzled. "What?"

"Michael Bradshaw." Leslie gave an impatient turn of her wrist. "You said he was the best magician in the country, but I've never heard of him. And what's he doing teaching at Georgetown?"

Winston smiled, relieved. "Well, I'll admit, that was something of a surprise to me, too. I guess all professional magicians aren't showboats, and it seems Bradshaw gave up performing some time ago to pursue the scholarly life. All the better for us, don't you see? An academic is bound to have more credibility with certain official representatives than an entertainer."

"But where did you find him?"

Winston leaned forward a little, as though imparting a confidence. "Well, it may impress you to know that I have a few contacts with the Magicians' Union and the Magic Castle in Las Vegas. No, don't smirk at me that way, young lady. I'll have you know that magicians are the most organized—and highly secretive—group of professionals in the world, and it's no small accomplishment to get on the inside. Which I'm not, precisely, I suppose," he was forced to admit, a trifle uncomfortably, "but my name—or the name of the Center—must have carried some weight, because when I explained what we needed they seemed to take me very seriously. And everyone I talked to, without hesitation, said the man we needed was Michael Bradshaw. The hierarchy among professional magicians is very strict, you see, and there didn't seem to be any question that Bradshaw was the very best. It didn't even matter that he wasn't a performing magician. In fact, I got the impression from the people I talked to that he was somehow too *good* to perform, as though there were some sort of unspoken rule about forced retirement." He lifted his shoulders in a gesture of conclusion. "At any rate, there's no doubt in my mind that he's good. If he could fool the three of you..." Wisely, Winston thought better of rubbing in that truth, and finished simply. "We're lucky to have him, Leslie, believe me."

"Or maybe he's lucky to have us," Leslie suggested thoughtfully. At Winston's questioning look she explained, "This could be the perfect chance for some free publicity for a man who's been offstage for a number of years and is perhaps just now thinking about returning. If he played his cards right, he could have this place in every major news magazine in the country inside a month."

And that, of course, was the real danger. For a man interested in furthering his own reputation, no opportunity could have been more perfect. If he took a stand against an unpopular public issue, if *he* was the recognized authority who was able to bring to light fraud in the use of public funds, if *he* was the man who could offer proof that the research going on at their center and others like theirs across the country was invalid, he would be proclaimed a hero and progress in the field would be set back fifty years or more. The truth was, of course, Leslie's first and foremost objective, but to a man as skillful and well-motivated as Bradshaw, the truth would be very easy to manipulate.

Winston seemed not in the least concerned. "Oh, I hardly think so," he replied. "One of the conditions Michael insisted upon before he would accept the job was that his name would not be used in connection with any of the publicity associated with the Center. I think it has something to do with a magician's code of ethics."

That, decided Leslie, almost as deflated as she was curious, made no sense whatever.

Winston looked at her patiently. "Look, Leslie, I don't understand the problem. I know the methods are a bit bizarre, but I thought you of all people would approve of the intent. You've always been half-skeptical of the results we get here anyway, and you certainly have no preconceived notions—pro or con—about psychic phenomena. You're always saying you need proof. Well…" He spread his hands. "Here it is."

Leslie shook her head, her expression adamant. "*Scientific* proof," she corrected tersely, "not this mumbo-jumbo and hat-full of kiddie-party tricks. For heaven's sake, Winston, don't you see this is exactly the kind of theatrics we *don't* need?"

But Winston, with the confidence of a man who is sitting on a fait accompli, only replied patiently, "Your worries are groundless, Leslie. But even if they weren't…" He shrugged. "It's done now, isn't it? If we want the funding, we keep the magician."

Leslie knew, as she had known from the beginning, that argument was worthless. But there was no resignation in her eyes as she got to her feet. "You and the federal government," she informed him caustically, "are the only two parties in the world who could have come up with such a solution."

He smiled at her, a bit condescendingly. "You're being unreasonable, you know."

She paused at the door to look back at him soberly. "I probably am," she agreed in a moment. "But I'm also right. And I think you know it."

She opened the door and left him without another word.

Leslie stepped out into the bright summer light with her thoughts still churning. Of course, on the surface everything Winston had said was true, but nothing within her strictly trained scientific mind would allow her to accept the solution he had devised. As far as she was concerned, there had never even been a problem, and this was exactly the kind of thing she had feared would happen when they got involved with federal funding. A magician. She was hard put not to groan out loud as she imagined the reactions of her parents—and other respected members of the scientific community just like them—if they ever found out. How was the work they did at the Center ever supposed to be taken seriously if they allowed themselves to be put on a level with card tricks and disappearing white rabbits?

The Center for the Study of Psi and Related Phenomena was located in the heart of the Maryland countryside, fifteen minutes from the children's hospital in one direction, fifteen minutes from Leslie's house in another, half an hour from the Bay and less than two hours from Washington, D.C. The Center was housed in a complex that some one hundred fifty years ago had been a rice plantation, and more recently had served as a boys' camp. The main house had been converted into a series of laboratories and staff offices; one sturdy stone outbuilding now housed the administrative section, and the bunkhouses had been converted into semimodern dormitories for those case subjects who traveled to the Center from out of town. The entire complex was picturesque, charming and quite atmospheric—with a coziness that lent a relaxed air Leslie felt was very helpful to their work, and a rather quaint aura of centuries of history, which some psychics claimed contributed greatly to their own energy flow.

But looking at it objectively for the first time in many years, Leslie had to admit some improvements were definitely in order. The old buildings, having withstood so much reconstruction and modernization over the years, had begun to sag, and there was a semiannual flooding problem in the administrative building. The dormitory roof was in need of repair, and they had been discussing for years the need to convert the dormitory arrangement into single-occupancy dwellings. For that matter, the wiring in the lab building was tenuous at best, and doubtlessly could not withstand another piece of high-voltage equipment, which was not to even mention the list of equipment they really should purchase.

She wondered dimly whether Michael Bradshaw would be staying at the Center during the summer, or traveling back and forth to Washington. Not that it mattered. Leslie intended to see as little of him as possible, and perhaps she would find a way to ignore his presence entirely.

As insidiously as an unbidden thought, Michael stepped from the shadows of the administration building and fell into step beside her. Though an irritated leap of her pulse registered his presence, Leslie did not look at him, and for a moment he simply strolled beside her, hands in pockets, eyes casually surveying the sun-washed landscape of the surrounding grounds—and damn it all, he *was* right; a little gardening would do wonders for the neglected grounds of the once-beautiful estate—and looking for all the world as though he had every right to be there, as though, in fact, their meeting was prearranged.

After a moment he inquired, "Where are we going?"

Leslie snapped open her purse, searching for her car keys. "I'm going to the children's hospital, where I have patients waiting. You," she informed him without looking up, "may go wherever you please."

"Hmm," he murmured. She could feel his eyes askance upon her. "Why is it that I get the feeling you have a particular place in mind?"

Leslie angled her footsteps toward the parking lot, still digging in her purse for her keys; he kept up with her. "I thought," he pointed out, "that you were supposed to show me around."

"Then you misunderstood." She couldn't seem to find her keys and, scowling, she went through the contents of her purse one more time. His presence beside her was a radiant thing, an energy source that was a strong rival even to the summer sun. Whatever else he was, Michael Bradshaw was impossible to ignore and that, not surprisingly, only irritated Leslie further.

"Oh, I hardly ever misunderstand, Dr. Roarke."

Leslie gave up on her keys and closed her purse with a snap. Still she did not look at him, and Michael kept in perfect step with her as they entered the small graveled parking lot. "How did you do it?" Leslie asked, making for her car, "with the tape recorder?"

She could feel the grin in his voice as he responded confidently, "A magician never reveals his secrets." Then as he saw her face tighten against him, he relented. "With magnets," he explained. "It's pretty standard fare."

"I see." She kept her voice even. Anyone could have done it, anyone with a rudimentary understanding of the nature of tape recordings and a little ingenuity. And that was disturbing—just as, no doubt, he had intended it to be.

"And before? In the booth." She had reached her car, and now she paused to look at him, squinting her eyes a little at the brilliant profile he made in the sunshine. His hair was a shimmering aureole of melted gold and milky cocoa, his face bronzed and mirror smooth, and his eyes were almost transparent. Even to look at him, in certain lights, was unsettling. "How did you control your vital signs readings like that? They were almost half the normal."

With his hands still in his pockets, he looked down at her studiously, appearing to debate whether or not to answer. When at last the corner of his lips turned upward a bit, the hint of the smile was slightly superior, deliberately enigmatic. "It could have been an ancient Yoga technique," he replied in the tone of voice one might use to pretend to impart a confidence while, in fact, revealing nothing at all, "or it could be that I tampered with your equipment beforehand." Then the smile widened into one of gentle enjoyment; a spark caught in the corner of his crinkled eyes. "I just love the age of technology, don't you? Everything is an illusion these days; magic is just around the corner wherever you turn."

"I told you," returned Leslie shortly, "I don't believe in magic." She opened her purse again, but the keys just weren't there. Scowling, she patted her pockets.

Michael's voice was curious. "Then why are you upset with me?"

"I don't know what you're talking about." Shading her eyes, she peered through the window of her locked car, half expecting to see the keys dangling from the ignition. "And I really don't have time to talk about it now; I've got other patients waiting." The keys weren't in the car. She had apparently left them in her office, which wasn't a bit like her. How embarrassing to have to go trudging back up the driveway with Michael Bradshaw dogging her every step after she had made it as clear as she possibly could that she did *not* want to talk to him.

"You're just a little bit inconsistent, you know," Michael said mildly.

"I've been called worse." She moved past him toward the drive; he followed.

"First you use a perfectly good psychology degree to work in a place like this," Michael continued implacably at her side. "Then you say you don't believe in what you're researching. Then you get angry with me because I'm trying to *prove* that what you don't believe in doesn't exist."

Leslie stopped and glared at him. "I *believe*," she told him deliberately, "in the truth. I believe in the scientific method and the right to investigate all unanswered questions. I don't like mysteries and I don't—" there was no possible way to mistake her meaning as her eyes swept him with vague contempt "—like lies."

He lifted one perspicacious eyebrow but did not seem in the least offended. He merely suggested perceptively, "Do you know what I think, Dr. Roarke? I don't think there's any kind of moral principle involved here at all. You're not upset because I've threatened your research or challenged the scientific method or even because I'm making you compromise your values. You're mad at me because I tricked you. Because I beat you at your own game."

That stung, and Leslie, whose understanding of human behavior was not limited to those other than herself, knew that an insult was not insulting unless it contained a grain of truth. In this particular case she had to admit that perhaps there was more than a grain of truth, which was precisely what irritated her. Yes, she was angry, and yes, she resented the fact that he had tricked her, but mostly she was angry with herself. Because she knew better, and the first time she had come close to allowing herself to believe in the unproven this was what had happened. It had been nothing more than a cheap trick.

She could feel the tinge of the sun on her cheeks, but hoped the anger did not glitter in her eyes as she carefully controlled her expression and faced him for another deliberate moment. She said, "We do serious work here, Mr. Bradshaw, whether or not you choose to accept it. It's difficult enough under normal circumstances; the last thing we need is someone like you coming in here and making a mockery of everything we're trying to do. I don't approve of you or your methods and I think everything about this project is a huge mistake. And in answer to your original question, the reason I'm upset with you is because I dislike deception in any form. And you, by your own admission, are deception personified."

"I see." His face was unreadable. "But I hope you won't let that in any way interfere with our personal relationship."

For a moment Leslie could do nothing but stare at him, incredulous. Then, collecting herself as smoothly as was possible, she replied, "I hardly see how it could, seeing as how we *have* no personal relationship."

"Everything is temporary in this world, Dr. Roarke," he assured her confidently.

And for just another moment she was speechless. The man was incredible. If ever there had been anyone who didn't know how to take no for an answer...

She didn't have the time—or the patience—to debate the matter today. Sooner or later he would have to be put in his place, but she knew that tackling that task would require a lot more mental fortitude than she was capable of generating right now. All she wanted to do at the moment was get away from this place, to the relative sanity of the Psychological and Social Services Department of the children's hospital, where hopefully she would find a way to put the events of the morning into perspective.

She said, somewhat stiffly, "Excuse me, please. As I told you before, I have other patients."

"Sure thing." He grinned at her amiably. "I'll meet you here then, bright and early in the morning, shall I? We can get started on my orientation then."

"I suspect you'll find yourself assigned to one of the other staff members by then," Leslie said coolly, and stepped past him. "Good day, Mr. Bradshaw."

Leslie had gone half a dozen steps up the driveway, toward her office, where her car keys must even now surely be waiting, when he called after her. She started to keep on walking, but after a moment's consideration, turned with a patient sigh. "What?" she demanded.

He stood where she had left him, still smiling, and he answered. "I just didn't want you to be late." He lifted his hand and tossed something across the sparkling gravel to her. "Have a good day now." And he turned and sauntered away.

Leslie caught the object instinctively, and as he walked away she opened her hand to stare at what she held.

Her car keys, what else?

Chapter Four

Leslie knew that one of the most common pitfalls of vacation season was post-vacation depression; it was therefore her custom to end her first day back at work with a little treat for herself. And after the hideous day she'd had, Leslie felt more than deserving of some sort of self-indulgence. Waiting for her in the bright, cheerful condo she had called home for the past three years was a fully stocked kitchen suggesting endless possibilities for gourmet meals, a bottle of duty-free French wine, and a brand-new paperback horror novel in which she planned to immerse herself until at least midnight.

The phone was ringing as she let herself in. Half inclined to simply let it ring, she took her time extracting the key from the lock, suppressing a groan as the telephone continued to shrill. Whoever it was was very persistent—but then so was everyone who dialed Leslie's number. That was what she got for being a doctor: no private life at all.

A hazy sunset was filtering through the picture windows as she reached for the telephone on the end table, shadowing a collection of framed lithographs and casting a yellow-green pall over the high-tech neatness of the room. Because she found the sight of the dying day vaguely depressing, Leslie reached with her other hand to draw the draperies as she spoke into the receiver.

"We drew straws to see who would call you," George said. "Where did you rush off to this afternoon?"

Leslie sighed as she sank onto the creamy beige sofa, kicking off her shoes. "I do have another job, George."

He snorted. "Don't give me that. You were mad as hell. And you know we have to discuss this."

Leslie combed her fingers through her hair, releasing a day's weariness with gentle massaging motions on her scalp. "Actually," she said, choosing her words carefully, "I thought it would be best if you and Malcolm discussed it between yourselves first. You're the head research scientists, after all, and you're going to be affected more directly by this than anyone else. I'm just a consultant, and I don't think I have any right to influence you with my opinion."

Again George made an unpleasant sound in his throat. "You're also a coward."

Leslie smiled crookedly. "Guilty."

"So are you interested in what we think?"

Not really, Leslie thought. *All I really want to do is open that bottle of wine and forget about this for a while.* But she had never been able to ignore her own overdeveloped sense of responsibility and she knew that, however hard she tried to make it otherwise, George and Malcolm did depend on her. She said, "I'll bet I can guess."

"Well, we were pretty upset at first," George admitted. "Insulted, outraged... Well, you saw that for yourself. And I still don't like the feel of the whole thing. I mean, a magician for Pete's sake! But..." And now his voice grew more restrained, thoughtful and reluctant. "Damn it, Leslie, maybe the man's got a point. We're dealing with human personalities here, and maybe machines and mathematical probabilities aren't the best standards by which to measure human potential. If we believe in what we're doing, why should we be rattled by a little outside intervention? On the other hand..." And now he released a long, frustrated sigh. "The whole thing still stinks, and he'd better not come poking around *my* lab while I'm working, I'll tell you that much. I'll deck the smart-mouthed little troublemaker.''

Leslie laughed, and it felt good to do so. "That's what I like, George, a man of decision!" She stretched out on the sofa to switch on a lamp, and the gloom dissipated into something very much like cheerfulness. Though her living quarters were not nearly as haphazardly decorated as her office, the mark of Leslie's personality was here, too, in the vibrant red and blue accent pieces that complemented her tasteful cream-colored furnishings, in hanging Tiffany lamps and wicker magazine stands. It was, generally, a nice place to come home to, and there was absolutely no reason why, tonight, it should suddenly seem so lonely.

"No, I mean it, Les." George's tone was as insistent as his tone, smooth and high-pitched for a man, could ever be. "I'm trying to be open-minded, and if this is what we have to do to ensure the grant, then so be it. But don't expect me to like it. And don't expect me to go out of my way to cooperate."

"And Malcolm? What does he think?"

"Take what I said and amplify it by ten or twenty decibels. All except the part about trying to cooperate, I mean. You know how Malcolm is. He takes everything personally."

"And you don't." It was a gentle remonstration, but in fact Leslie was stalling for time. She knew George was waiting for her to either support their position or contradict it, and she knew that whatever she said would carry enough weight to ultimately influence their behavior. If she took a stand on the side of Michael Bradshaw, the two men might object but they would eventually be swayed by her opinion. But if the three of them presented a firm and united front against him, they could most possibly end the program in a matter of weeks. But what would happen to the clinic if they refused the conditions of that grant?

It was a weighty responsibility. Damn it, how could she tell Malcolm and George that Michael Bradshaw was the best thing that had ever happened to them when in fact she agreed with everything they were saying one hundred percent? And why did they have to rely so heavily upon her to guide their judgment?

As her silence lengthened, George prompted predictably, "Well? Don't you have an opinion?"

Again Leslie chuckled, though this time evasively. "You know me, George. Never one to make a snap judgment." For the moment that was the best she could do for Michael Bradshaw. And it was still a great deal more than he deserved.

She knew George was disappointed in her but she didn't know what else to say. She made it a policy to stay as detached as possible from developments at the clinic—how else could she maintain an open mind—and she simply wasn't prepared to wade into a fight like this. She said, somewhat apologetically, "Look, George, it's been a really long day and I haven't had dinner yet. Why don't we all give ourselves some time to think this over? There's nothing we can do tonight at any rate. Let's give it a couple of days and we'll all talk later in the week, okay?"

"You're not being very helpful," George replied, disgruntled, and as she said goodbye Leslie had to admit to herself that she most definitely was not.

For a moment she sat on the sofa, deep in thought and trying not to become morose. She had known, of course, that George and Malcolm would not let her off the hook so easily—this was the biggest professional crisis the Center had ever faced, and it would take a lot more than merely walking off the grounds to disassociate herself from the problem. She had tried to lose herself in her work at the children's hospital, but with no patients to see, there was only paperwork to greet her return and the only thing she hated worse than making administrative decisions was paperwork.

Damn Michael Bradshaw anyway. Leslie scowled as she got to her feet, irritated that he should invade her peace of mind even here, in the sanctity of her own home. He was so cocky. She was quite certain he could turn out to be a

first-rate pest if she gave him half the chance. That business
with the car keys... Of all the nerve. Who was he trying
to impress, anyway?

Whatever his intention, there was no arguing the fact that
he had succeeded in impressing her. It hadn't taken a magician's trick to do it, either. No matter how hard she tried,
she couldn't seem to erase that distinctive profile, that
smooth and unreadable face, from her mind. She wished
she had never allowed him to flirt with her this morning.
She could have stopped it if she had wanted to, but she had
done everything but blatantly encourage him. And she had
enjoyed every minute of it. Somehow she was certain that
things wouldn't seem so unmanageable now if she hadn't
ventured that small uncertain step over the line between
professional and personal judgment, if she hadn't, for that
very brief and tenuous time, allowed herself to like him.

Leslie determinedly pushed Michael Bradshaw from her
mind as she went into the kitchen. One of Leslie's most
extravagant pleasures was cooking, and the preparation of
a gourmet meal was the one sure way she knew to improve
her mood.

She had bought the condo for its investment potential,
and in all other ways she looked at it as just that—an investment. Its furnishings were tasteful and restrained, its
maintenance so diligently seen to that it was almost sterile,
and in every way it announced the presence of a discreetly
successful, value-conscious and upwardly mobile professional—except in the kitchen.

The kitchen was easily the largest room in the house.
She had removed the dividing wall between kitchen and
formal dining room, replaced the carpet with hand-layed
brick throughout, installed a built-in dining nook of teak
and brass, and expanded her counter and cabinet space by
half. Lining these counters were a multitude of mismatched
pottery canisters and covered jars, each containing its own
blend of special spices, leavens, and hard-to-find food
items. A fresh herb garden completely filled one window;
avocado, tomato plants and pepper trees were terraced be-

neath another. Her stove was in a center island with work space on either side; above it was suspended a complete collection of copper saucepans; below it, not very neatly stacked, were her iron skillets and dutch ovens. Recipes yet to be tried were tacked on a bright yellow bulletin board next to the oven, and an open shelf sagged under the weight of her cookbooks.

Taking down her favorite cookbook now, Leslie perched on a butcher-block cabinet, her spirits rising considerably as she thumbed through the well-worn pages in anticipation of the treat she was about to give herself. The pages were swollen with moisture and stained with the remnants of many a superb meal—no one had ever told Leslie that in order to be a good cook one also has to be neat—and she scanned each recipe faithfully, though she knew them most by heart. She had a taste for something really exotic, rich with cream sauce and delicately balancing spice and smoothness.

The telephone rang again and she reached for it absently, her greeting much more charitable this time.

"Well, it's about damn time you got home." Her father's voice was gruff. "Didn't you get my messages?"

Leslie sighed, patience taught by long experience. "Of course I did, Daddy, as soon as I checked in with the hospital this morning. If you wanted to reach me, you should have left a message on my machine—or at the Center."

He gave an uncharitable snort. "If I were to leave a message over there, the first thing you know is I'd have my name associated with the place. It's bad enough to have my daughter's name connected with it, although fortunately not too many people recognize it."

Leslie turned a page, accustomed enough to her father's bluntness to ignore it. "How's Mom?"

"She's fine. She sends her best. Her team is beginning to make a breakthrough on the genetic-splicing project. It's causing a lot of excitement. You'll probably be reading about her in the next *Scientific Journal*. They're expecting to make an announcement any day now."

The comparison between her mother's accomplishments and Leslie's own was implicit and not so easy to ignore. It was a deliberate and mean-spirited effort on her father's part to remind Leslie of her so-called failure by pointing out the triumphs of others, as though he were constantly saying to her "Look where you came from—and look where you are now!" He was trying to make her feel small and ashamed, and more often than not he succeeded.

Usually Leslie was not so quick to rise to the bait, but tonight she couldn't help herself. "How wonderful for you both," she responded sweetly. "And now that you ask, I'm doing quite well, too."

"And how many ghosts have you exorcised this week?" He grunted.

"One doesn't exorcise ghosts, Daddy. One exorcises demons. And because I never took the vows, I'm afraid I'm not qualified to perform that service." She turned another page in the cookbook, not even bothering to read the previous one.

"Maybe you would have been better off if you *had* taken the vows." His voice was very smooth, drawling almost, the way it got when was bordering on sarcasm. "Do you have any idea how much it cost to put you through college and graduate school? Just take a guess, my dear."

"I don't have to guess. I know to the penny. Do you want your money back?"

"No. I want to know how much you're making now."

"Public service is traditionally underpaid, Daddy." Her voice was dripping with sarcasm and she knew she was reacting like a twelve-year-old, but that was another one of her father's most effective tricks—to bring out the worst in her and then make her feel guilty because she was acting badly. So what? she defended herself irritably, trying to concentrate on the ingredients required for a lobster souffle. That expensive education had not come complete with a guarantee to make her perfect, and there was no law that said a practicing psychologist could not regress to adolescent behavior every now and then. As a matter of fact, she was of the strong opinion that it was therapeutic.

"Exactly!" declared her father on a note of triumph. "Public service is exactly what I'm talking about. It would be another matter entirely if you were actually doing something worthwhile, fulfilling a need or performing a service, but nothing galls me more than a talented, educated and skilled professional wasting time and the God-given right to *practice* that profession—"

Leslie thought she had been patient long enough. And she was getting hungry. "What did you call about, Daddy?" she interrupted.

Her father didn't miss a beat. Another thing about men as confident and overbearing as Dr. Amos Roarke—it was impossible to insult them. "I'm going to be in the city on the twentieth," he announced imperiously. "I want you to join me for dinner."

Washington was the only city in this part of the country her father recognized; it would never occur to him to clarify his destination—any more than it would occur to him that if he wanted to meet his daughter for dinner he might have chosen some place a bit more convenient than a restaurant two hours away. Leslie knew, of course, that he was not flying in to have dinner with her; he doubtlessly had some business in Washington and decided to take the opportunity to do his familial duty at the same time, effectively getting it out of the way for another year or so. Leslie didn't know how she would react if once, just once, he would call her just to talk to her, or ask to see her just because he missed her.

She said, stalling, "Will Mom be coming?"

"Of course not," he scoffed. "She's much too busy. I can only make it myself by taking a couple of hours away from the convention—which I *shouldn't* be doing. I'm supposed to be giving an address at dinner that night; I had to get Warren Isaacs to take my place."

So, it was just as she had figured. Not only was she an

afterthought to him, but he was determined to make her feel guilty about that as well.

"Seven o'clock at the Terrace," he was saying. "And that's firm. Don't be late."

Leslie didn't want to go. She really, really didn't want to go. But, because he was her father, she answered, "All right. I'll see you then."

"And for God's sake, wear a dress, will you? And put on some makeup or something."

Leslie bit back a retort, then found she was biting her lip. Damn, the things that man could do to her. "Goodbye, Daddy. I'll see you soon."

He had hung up before she finished speaking.

Leslie replaced the receiver, took a deep breath, and straightened her shoulders. Bad luck comes in threes, so they say, and between Michael Bradshaw, George's temper tantrum and her father, she figured she had just about had her dose for the day. The meeting with her father was several weeks away, George and Malcolm were just going to have to take care of themselves, and Michael Bradshaw... Well, she would deal with him when the time came. Tonight all she had ahead of her was a gourmet meal, a glass of wine and a paperback thriller, and she was going to enjoy all of them to the fullest.

She sprang down from the counter as a recipe caught her eye. Shrimp curry. That was exactly what she wanted. She hated to use canned shrimp, but she wasn't too dogmatic to compromise when the occasion called for it, and the sauce would be so luscious the inferior quality of the shrimp wouldn't matter.

She was pleased with how easily she had banished incipient depression, and as she busily began opening cabinets and taking down utensils she only had to pause once to stifle an intrusive thought. That was when she caught herself wondering what Michael was doing for dinner tonight.

IT WAS NOT EXACTLY the *Queen Mary*, but the thirty-foot cruiser was freshly painted, almost completely outfitted, and with some minor engine work, would actually be seaworthy. And to Michael Bradshaw it was home.

He had taken advantage of the free afternoon to move the last of his books and papers from his Georgetown apartment onto the boat—at least the ones he would be needing over the summer—and he had been somewhat dismayed by the fact that the apartment still looked as though it was the last refuge for the world's cast-off collectibles, despite the fact that he had already removed everything he had any anticipation of using. It was late by the time he finished arranging everything—forced by close quarters to be more methodical than he ever was with his apartment, and he sat on deck watching the sunset until dinnertime, thinking mostly about Dr. Leslie Roarke.

He was still thinking about her as he went below and began to gather the ingredients and set about the preparations for dinner. He had a sudden and acute taste for shrimp curry, and the pound of fresh shrimp he had bought this morning with no special plans in mind would be perfect.

The living quarters were not particularly spacious, nor elaborately furnished. The sitting room/bedroom was equipped with a love seat, two comfortable chairs and a writing desk, everything scaled down in size to accommodate the somewhat sparse floor space, except the bed, which was queen-size and comfortable, located between the two forward portholes that caught the morning sun and provided a fresh sea breeze all night. The walls were lined with high shelves for his books and a built-in unit accommodated a small television set and stereo. An elaborately decorated seaman's chest against one wall held all the necessary accoutrements of his trade, without which he traveled nowhere.

But the small, efficient galley was stocked with all the conveniences of any modern gourmet kitchen and was, in Michael's opinion, the highlight of the entire cruiser. He had learned to cook at an early age from necessity, and it was in his temperament that he did not consider a thing worth doing unless it could be done superlatively.

He began to wash and peel the shrimp with the same lightning-quick grace and digital dexterity with which he might have worked a deck of cards or turned fire into snow, whistling a cheerful tune under his breath, musing about Leslie Roarke. He was trying to explain to himself, in fact, why she had stayed so much on his mind and what it was about her that simply wouldn't leave him alone. It wasn't as though she was the sexiest woman he had ever seen, although he had to admit there was a certain sensuous grace about the way she held herself, and moved her hands, and crossed her legs—all without a shred of artifice or contrivance on her part—that went straight to the primitive in him. He had never been particularly attracted to blondes, especially artificial ones, but the way her hair caressed her collarbone, curving slightly, pale silk against lightly tanned skin, stayed with him. All in all, Michael knew more beautiful women, certainly more approachable ones, and the odds were that he could make a single phone call and be with one of them tonight. It was just as well he didn't have a phone, because the only person he really wanted to be with was Leslie.

It was her face, he decided. A sensitive, perceptive face filled with a great capacity for compassion and humor and understanding. It was a face that invited confidence but was unaccustomed to giving it, a face that spoke of tenderness she was too little used to receiving. And her eyes, warm and wide-set and multicolored, with a capability for lightning flashes of mood...and temper. He almost chuckled out loud as he remembered the way those eyes had darkened when he walked into the administration office this afternoon. Like storm clouds aching to burst, but held in check by that magnificent control of hers. He was ashamed of the feeling of almost boyish satisfaction it had given him to make her lose control, even for the briefest of moments, this afternoon.

Intriguing, that's what she was. And the last thing in the

world Michael needed was to get involved with an intriguing woman. He knew better than anyone that the challenge of the unknown—or the unattainable—was more appealing than a blatant invitation, and ultimately more seductive.

He dumped the fresh shrimp into a pot of boiling water, and then stepped back a little from the steam, a faint and momentary frown marring his brow. Why, he wondered, was he having dinner alone when the most interesting woman he had met in a long time was less than half an hour away?

It would be foolish to go over there, of course. For one thing, she was mad as hell at him right now and needed some time to cool off. For another, she was definitely not the kind of woman who liked to be rushed. And for another—and this was perhaps the most important reason— he was not entirely sure what it was he wanted from her, and despite her aura of self-sufficiency, he knew she was fragile, vulnerable, easily frightened away. The last thing he wanted to do was give her more cause for building up defenses.

He opened an overhead cabinet and surveyed its contents thoughtfully. A meal like this would have to be topped with something not too rich, not too heavy....

On the other hand, he did have a job to do. Things were not going to be made any easier by the fact that the whole professional staff was working against him. His work was important, to her as well as to him and to the Center itself, if only she could be made to admit that.

Chocolate mousse, he decided, and in so thinking, a relaxed and confident smile spread over his face. He wouldn't rush her. He wouldn't frighten her. But some things, he supposed, were simply predestined.

"OUTSIDE, THE WIND HOWLED. But was it the wind, or the sound of breathing? Something huge and dark and stealthy, blowing its fetid breath as it moved closer...and closer...."

Leslie nearly dropped the book she was reading into the

bath water. She jumped and sat up straight in the bathtub, water cascading from her shoulders and leaving a froth of bubbles on her chin as she looked around the steamy room, her ears alert to a sound she had heard. From the lawn outside the high bathroom window came an annoyed yowl and the scampering of tiny feet, and she relaxed, smiling at her own foolishness. She sank back into the water and picked up her wineglass, turning a page and leaving another damp thumbprint upon the already humid paper.

Dinner had been wonderful, the phone hadn't rung again, and now on her second glass of wine, she was beginning to recover from the unsettling events of the day. The dishes were done, she hadn't thought of Michael Bradshaw more than half a dozen times all evening, and now she reflected as she settled back into the engrossing tale of horror and suspense that the only thing that had been missing from the evening was dessert. Chocolate pudding would be nice. It wouldn't take long to prepare, and the way she made it, with thick yellow cream and freshly shaved chocolate, it was almost as good as a mousse.

"The boy huddled in the corner, his small chest rising and falling rapidly, his terror-filled eyes searching the darkness. And from the darkness, a single eye opened, and looked back...."

Leslie shivered and closed the book, laying it carefully on the carpet as she prepared to get out of the tub. Reading in the bathtub had seemed like a great idea, but she hadn't counted on the shrouded mists of steam, the stealthy noises of the building's creaking and settling that sounded so much like footsteps, and the uncomfortable recollections of *Psycho* that it would evoke. This seemed like the perfect time to make dessert.

She toweled off her body briskly and methodically and wrapped herself in a short white terry robe. She unwrapped her freshly shampooed hair and tossed the towel aside, grimacing in the mirror at the witch's strands that tangled over her face and crept down her neck. Her mother always said that Leslie was the only person she knew who had been born with dark roots, and was constantly badgering her daughter to do something about them—besides being a brilliant scientist, her mother was also beautiful, well-groomed, and perfect in every way—but Leslie had always shied away from engaging in the constant battle it would require to improve on nature. She supposed one day her hair would make up its mind whether it intended to be blond or brown, and until then, she wasn't going to worry about it.

She combed out the tangles with her fingers, deciding to blow-dry her hair later, and made one final face at the gaunt-looking, waiflike creature who stared back at her in the mirror. She picked up her wineglass and her book and left the bathroom, intent on chocolate pudding.

She knew her privacy had been invaded even before she saw the signs. It was a spooky feeling, a sensation of something just a little bit out of place, nothing she could define but something definitely amiss.... And then, her steps cautious and her senses alert, she entered the living room and saw the coffee table.

She approached it slowly. Two silver candles burned on either end, casting a wavering, golden glow about the room. Between them, on a crystal serving dish, was what looked very much like a chocolate mousse. And before it a thick vellum card was propped. Leslie picked up the card cautiously. In beautiful black Gothic lettering it read, "A small peace offering. If you would care to call a truce, I am waiting at your front door."

Leslie read the card twice, then a third time. Hesitantly, as though afraid it would dissolve at her touch, she dipped a finger into the fluffy chocolate concoction and tasted it. Real chocolate mousse. And quite good, too.

Leslie crossed the room and opened the front door. "So," she said. "You're as good at breaking and entering as you are at picking pockets."

Michael looked down at her politely. "I beg your pardon?"

Leslie didn't move from her guarded position at the threshold. "You stole my car keys," she accused.

His brow wrinkled with slight puzzlement in the uncertain candlelight from the living room. "Funny. I seem to recall *giving* them to you, not taking them from you."

"Very cute. You picked my pocket."

His face relaxed into a persuasive smile. "A minor feat of prestidigitation, my dear," he assured her. "How else was I going to get you to stay long enough to talk to me?" And then, "May I come in?"

Silly question, Leslie thought irritably, since it was abundantly obvious he had already *been* in. He had changed from his attire of the morning into charcoal slacks and a white shirt, open to mid chest, cuffs casually turned up. His hair was fluffy and shiny and brushed away from his face; he looked cool and fresh and comfortable and reminded Leslie acutely of her wet, straggly hair and her bulky bathrobe—and of her nakedness beneath the robe.

Self-consciously she drew the belt a bit tighter around her waist and stepped away from the door ungraciously. "You might as well," she said irritably. *Damn*, why hadn't she taken the time to dry her hair before leaving the bathroom?

"Most men would have settled for a box of candy," she commented somewhat dryly, and flipping on a lamp, bent to blow out the candles

"The difference between the pedestrian and genuine style," he responded, and though she did not look at him she could sense his eyes moving around the room, absently surveying, lazily taking note of everything—including Leslie, in her short terry robe and her ratty hair. When she turned to face him again there was no doubt in her mind that he knew she was naked beneath, and why that should bother her she couldn't imagine.

"What do you want?" she said abruptly.

If her rudeness surprised him, he gave no indication. He merely stood in the center of the room, a pointed reminder that she had not asked him to be seated and had no intention of doing so, and looked thoughtful. "At the moment," he decided at last, "I think we should concentrate on establishing a more comfortable working relationship. And the only way to do that is for you to come to terms with your hostility toward me.''

"Oh, for goodness sake!'' Leslie said irritably. "I'm supposed to be the psychologist around here. Sit down.''

"Thank you,'' he returned politely, "but I won't be staying that long. I don't want to wear out my welcome. I would just like you to ask yourself one question—who is it really going to help if you make my job more difficult?''

It was very awkward, standing in the middle of the room—she half-naked and he fully clothed and utterly composed—discussing uncomfortable professional matters. But even more difficult was the fact that he had only voiced the question she had been asking herself all evening, and that the only possible answer sounded selfish, immature and very unworthy of her.

Leslie had already been made to feel like a twelve-year-old once this evening; she was not about to open herself up to more of the same from this enigmatic, overbearing, very attractive stranger. He was right; it was time she came to terms with it.

She said, "You already know why I disapprove of your involvement with the Center.''

"I know what you've told me,'' he said shrewdly. "I think it's a bit more complicated than that.''

"Maybe it is,'' Leslie admitted. She brushed a clinging strand of damp hair away from her collarbone and when she saw his eyes follow the movement she quickly dropped her hand. "But you've got to understand the kind of ridicule and skepticism we are faced with constantly. It's easy to become defensive.''

He tilted his head at a slight angle, appearing to consider this, and Leslie found that an enormously appealing gesture. Almost endearing. "I can understand that,'' he said. "What I don't understand is why you should feel defensive against me when we're both working toward the same goal—the truth.''

A good point. And again, it was not something that she

hadn't considered before. She moved her hands impatiently, signifying frustration, and crossed the room toward the kitchen. "You're not interested in the truth," she replied. "You only want to prove your point. As far as I'm concerned, you've proven it. Even the best of us can be fooled by a fast talker and a smooth mover, and…" She returned from the kitchen, dessert dishes and silverware in her hands, and met his eyes evenly, "Science is redundant in the face of magic."

She thought she saw a brief spark of admiration in his eyes, though for the life of her she couldn't imagine why it should be there, and he murmured, "You make me sound very cold-hearted."

Leslie sat on the edge of the sofa and began to serve the mousse. "Aren't you?"

"I've never thought so."

He came over to her with his usual catlike swiftness and grace, that motion that was as subtle and as untrackable as the wind in the leaves, and it was possibly only the unexpectedness of his presence beside her that caused Leslie to catch her breath. She thought he would sit beside her, but when she handed a dish of chocolate mousse to him he only set it on the coffee table and took her hand instead, drawing her to her feet.

She could feel her heart speed a fraction as she looked into the smooth, unreadable face, and the only thing she could think was that surely he did not intend to kiss her now, with her wet, tangled hair and her scruffy bathrobe and her bare feet. His hand was strong, warm and sinewy around hers, his body close and lean and radiating kinetic power. She caught the tangy scent of his cologne and could sense, rather than feel, the gentle rise and fall of his breath.

Her lips parted instinctively, though whether in anticipation or protest she did not know, and then he smiled. "I'll make a deal with you, Dr. Roarke," he said. "You try to be open-minded about my work, and I'll remain open-minded about yours."

"Sounds like a contest." Leslie's voice was a little

husky, and that was embarrassing. He still held her hand, close to his thigh, but not touching it.

"Perhaps it is. I still think I could teach you to believe in magic. All I need is a chance."

"That's absurd." Leslie gave a small tug on her hand, but he did not release it. "We're talking about two different things, and I'm not in the least bit interested in learning about magic."

Again the small, enigmatic curve of his lips. "Then I have my work cut out for me, don't I?"

Leslie could feel her skin flushing beneath her robe and her pulse continued to accelerate. How was he doing that? He was barely touching her. He had made not a single suggestive move nor said a word that could be construed as seductive, but her body was reacting to him as forcefully as though he had taken her into an embrace. Leslie knew that she had to disengage herself before she began to look very foolish.

She said, forcing a tone that was calm and reasonable, "All right. You deserve a chance to do your job. I still don't approve, but as long as I'm certain you're acting...ethically..." She gave another small, experimental tug on her hand. "And that you're not deliberately doing anything to interfere with our work, I won't stand in your way."

"Fair enough. You take your road and I'll take mine, and we'll see who gets to the truth first."

She met his gaze evenly. "I'll be watching you every minute."

"I'll be counting on it," he assured her smoothly. And then he released her hand. Leslie was not certain whether she was relieved or disappointed, but at least she could breathe again.

She turned quickly back to the coffee table. "Don't you want your dessert? I can make some coffee."

"No, thank you, I won't stay. This was all I wanted for tonight."

"Oh." She turned to him and hoped that puzzlement was

all she was feeling, and all that was showing in her eyes.
"Well, then..." She started for the door, expecting him to
follow. "Thank you—for the dessert and—"

"Don't bother to see me out," he said pleasantly behind
her. "I'll leave the way I came."

"Well, I'm sorry if I was rude before and I hope you
don't think that I—"

She turned, but the room was empty. A second earlier
he had been right behind her, and now, without prelude or
fanfare, he was gone.

She stood there for quite some time, a slightly puzzled,
slightly amused smile on her face, and then she went back
into the living room to enjoy some of the best chocolate
mousse she had ever tasted. One thing was for certain: the
summer was not going to be dull.

Chapter Five

Karen and Kevin Gaynor were twenty years old, and so
much alike that it would have been impossible to tell them
apart were it not for the difference in gender—and even so,
it was sometimes difficult. Their dark hair was cropped in
identical pageboy styles, they wore consistently matching
jeans, T-shirts and sneakers, and even the pattern of freck-
les across each nose was a carbon copy of the other. Their
gestures were often in unison, their expressions were the
same, and even their voices were hard to tell apart at times.
Clinically, Leslie thought that wasn't a very healthy way
to live, and had the two been under her treatment rather
than her evaluation, she would have instituted a program
of separateness without delay, beginning with a shopping
trip and a visit to the hair stylist for Karen. She doubted
whether the girl had ever even owned a pair of stockings.

The two had been discovered in a routine research project involving telepathy among twins. They had scored
markedly higher than the norm on tests for telepathy, which
was interesting in itself, but more than that, they seemed
to possess some sort of joint telekinetic ability that definitely merited further study. They were staying at the Center for the summer, cheerful volunteers for a study of the
abilities they still saw as no more than a parlor game. Until
Michael Bradshaw had come along and turned the Center

upside down with his phony magic, they had been the most exciting thing to happen to psychic research in decades.

They were in Leslie's office now, growing a little restless with all the boring questions she was asking them. The two formerly sweet-tempered kids had become somewhat spoiled by all the attention given them since they had arrived here and, frankly, were beginning to turn into applause-seeking show-offs. Considering their basic pattern of insecurity and uncertain self-esteem, this was not surprising, but they were not making Leslie's job any easier.

"Say, what has our dad got to do with anything, anyway?" Kevin demanded now, squirming his small-framed body in the chair. "I thought it was us you were interested in. The things we can do."

"What I'm interested in," explained Leslie patiently, "is how you are able to do the things you do. Your father died when you were very young, Kevin, and sometimes it takes a crisis like that to trigger hidden strengths—to change our lives, if you will. You and Karen became much closer after your father's death, didn't you?"

Kevin shrugged. "We were always close; I've told you that. We always knew what the other was thinking." And then he considered. "Maybe it got a little easier then. Like a spark that caught—something that had always been there but never had anything to set it off before then. Yeah, I guess that's about the way it was."

Leslie made a surreptitious note of his choice of words. Their father had died in an explosion.

"Can I ask you something, Dr. Roarke?" Karen had been wandering around the room, examining Leslie's pictures, her framed quilting squares, the books on her shelves. Though Karen had contributed nothing for the past five minutes and seemed, in fact, to be paying no attention whatsoever to the conversation between Leslie and Kevin, Leslie knew she had not missed a word.

Karen picked up a framed photograph on Leslie's desk, glanced at it briefly, and continued, "What good do you think all this is doing? I mean, this is a nice place to spend the summer and all..." She gestured vaguely toward the tangled-pasture view from the window, "it's not like some of it hasn't been pretty interesting...but when you're finished studying us, what then? I mean, what good is it going to do us? Are we going to write a book and get rich and famous or something?"

Leslie smiled. "You might do that, I suppose. Or it might be enough for you just to understand a bit more about yourselves and how you function."

Karen shrugged, unimpressed. "It doesn't seem to me there's much point in being able to do things other people can't if you can't make a profit on it, somehow."

Leslie thought in dismay, *Good Lord, who put that idea into her head? Before they came here they were just two confused kids with a secret. Now they're thinking about how to exploit that secret for profit....*

Sensing her disapproval, Karen defended herself, "I've seen lots of books about things like this, written by people who aren't half as good as we are. I mean, it's not as though we have a burning desire to spend the rest of our lives as poor college students. There's nothing wrong with wanting to better yourself is there?"

"Of course not," Leslie said gently. She noted the second reference to fire. "But being in the center ring of the circus isn't always all it's cracked up to be—you told me that yourself. It might bring you more problems than it's worth."

Karen looked half agreeable, half reluctant, and Kevin changed the subject easily. "We're trying something new, Dr. Roarke," he said with the sly, teasing eagerness of one who has a secret he's dying to tell. "We don't want to show anyone until we're sure we can do it."

"Oh?" Leslie looked at him with interest. "Can you tell me about it?"

Karen smiled. "It's better if you see it."

Leslie was used to the two of them answering for each other—another symptom of confused identity that Leslie made a conscientious attempt to rectify. "I was talking to

Kevin, Karen," she reminded her with a smile, and the twins shared a mischievous look.

"It's better if you see it," Kevin repeated cooperatively, and Leslie couldn't help grinning. Sometimes they were imps, sometimes they were angels, but all the time they were a challenge.

"All right," she said, pushing back from her desk and crossing her legs. "That's it for today. Why don't you—"

The door opened, and Michael looked in. "Sorry," he said, and started to back out. "I didn't know you were busy."

"Oh, that's all right," Karen volunteered quickly. "We're all finished here."

Michael came inside, and there was no mistaking the star-struck look Karen cast him. *Uh-oh*, Leslie thought, noticing the way Kevin's face darkened. *Trouble.*

"Hi, Michael," Karen said, and her thin, angular body seemed suddenly softer, more colorful, more feminine. A crush at the very least, Leslie observed, and watched Kevin, whose eyes were growing stormier by the minute.

Michael returned her smile casually. "How's it going, Karen? Kevin?"

Kevin got to his feet abruptly, and before she even looked at him, Karen's expression had changed, becoming more guarded and a little embarrassed, tinged with a trace of disappointment. "We have to be going," Kevin said, starting for the door. "See you around, Dr. Roarke."

Karen gave Michael a fleeting smile at the door before she quickly followed her brother out.

"She's got a crush on you," Leslie commented.

"And he's jealous as hell," Michael finished for her, but dismissed it with a slight lift of his eyebrows as he came over to her and took the chair Kevin had just vacated. "Odd pair."

"You don't seem very concerned," Leslie said somewhat testily, closing the open file on the Gaynors and putting it away in her drawer. "But then I suppose you're accustomed to impressionable young girls falling at your feet.''

That was a stupid thing to say, both for its childishness and because it made an open acknowledgment of what they both already knew—that he was a very, very attractive man. Leslie couldn't believe she had said it, and impatience with the fact that he could so easily rattle her only compounded the inexplicably thorny temper that had overtaken her the minute he walked into the room. Only one other man had ever been able to so effortlessly reduce her to the emotional and behavioral status of a twelve-year-old—her father.

Michael chuckled, his eyes dancing with unabashed amusement over her discomfiture. ''Actually, it's been ages since I had an impressionable young girl fall at my feet. I find I rather like it—especially as mature, professional and sophisticated types seem to be going out of their way to ignore me lately.''

Without giving her a chance to react to that—which was just as well, because Leslie had no sharp-witted reply ready—he added mildly, ''And why should I be concerned, pray tell? What do you think they're going to do, zap me with the evil eye?''

In the past four days Michael had begun to settle into the Center. He was introduced to staff and case subjects alike as a professor from Georgetown who was joining the staff for the summer as a consultant and observer, and no one questioned. True to her word, Leslie had maintained a distant but tolerant attitude toward his work, and just as she had expected, Malcolm and George followed suit, though somewhat more reluctantly.

So far everything was going smoothly, and perhaps that was what irritated her most. Michael had been discreet, alert and annoyingly taciturn, asking his questions, making his observations, and offering absolutely no judgments. Leslie had expected by now that he would have had the entire place in an uproar; instead, he was making friends of the case subjects and earning the respect of the lower staff members, who had no reason to believe he was any-

thing other than a professor with interest in psychic phenomena. Leslie had not been alone with him since the night
of the chocolate mousse, and perhaps that was the reason
it really rankled to see him stroll so casually into her office
in his body-hugging cotton sweater and jacket with its mod-
ish oversized sleeves pushed up above the elbow and the
dark slacks that looked better on him than they had any
right to. Leslie had been geared up for a fight all week and
she felt cheated that he hadn't given it to her.

She said now, reaching to extract the tape of the Gaynor
session from the machine, "Those two are very protective
of each other—and highly volatile. I just wish you wouldn't
stir up things between them." She paused with the cassette
tape in her hand and looked at him suspiciously. "Do you
have any magnets in your pockets today?"

He grinned and spread his hands, inviting, "Search me."

Oh, cute, Bradshaw, very cute. Maybe one of the things
that bothered her most about him was his ability to put her
in a consistently bad humor while never once losing his
sunny disposition.

Leslie tucked away the cassette and sat back in her chair,
her expression cool and untroubled. "What do you want?"

The slightest hint of a playful smile curved his lips. It
was easy to see how Karen had developed a crush on him.
Very easy. "Why do I have to want anything? Maybe I
just missed you."

She had missed him, too, absurd as it was. He had caused
her more aggravation in a shorter period of time than anyone she had ever met, but his sudden withdrawal from her
life was ominous...like waiting for the other shoe to drop.
She didn't know him very well at all, but she knew him
well enough to realize that his exemplary behavior since he
had joined the staff of the Center was a smoke screen, and
she wondered what he was up to.

She said casually, "Have you found anything interesting
since you've been here?"

"Besides you, you mean?"

It was uttered in the most off-hand way, wonderfully

understated, an old magician's trick used to catch the mark off guard. Leslie watched as he picked up a sterling silver letter opener from her desk, examining it with cursory interest as he sat back and rested one ankle on his knee, looking as though he was prepared to stay for awhile. Leslie felt she should scowl at him but couldn't quite manage it. Her eyes were drawn instead to the long and skillful fingers that balanced the letter opener, masterful hands with sensual grace, as fascinating to look at as any other part of him.

She moved her eyes away from his hands and addressed his question dryly. "Besides me. You haven't forgotten your purported reason for being here, have you?"

"How could I?" A spark of friendly mischief played in his eyes. "I have a personal challenge to face now, as well as a professional one. Remember our agreement?"

"All I remember agreeing to is that we would both do our jobs and stay out of each other's way." She wondered how he kept his hair so thick and full. She wondered— clinically, of course—how it would feel to the touch.

"I remember it being a bit more complicated than that." For a moment that wonderful smile teased the softening corners of his lips again, then he reverted to business. Leslie found that somewhat disappointing. "Actually, I haven't done much of anything this week except get acquainted with the operation, see how everything functions, get to know everyone's job. You're my last stop."

How nice, Leslie thought wryly, *to be just another stop on someone's list.* But she said, "Saving the best for last, huh?"

His eyes flashed easy appreciation for her relaxed manner and he agreed lazily, "In a way. Except that what I'm really saving for last has nothing to do with business—and it really *is* the best."

Lord, thought Leslie, a little weakly, *he's good at this.* Subtle innuendo, drowsy smiles, inviting stances—each and every movement designed to make her aware of him, receptive to him, relaxed with him. And it was working. She could feel the chemistry generate even as they spoke, initial hostility and suspicion dissolving into simple enjoyment of feeling like a woman, into amused anticipation for what he would do next.

Because the gentle gleam in his eyes—no matter how much she enjoyed it—was beginning to work on her composure, and this was, after all, a professional office, Leslie said, "So. What flagrant examples of fraud have you uncovered so far?"

He clicked his tongue reprovingly against his teeth. "Now, now, Dr. Roarke, is that a trace of hostility I detect in your tone? I thought we'd gotten past that."

"Not hostility, just curiosity." Of their own volition, her eyes were drawn again to the absent motions of his fingers as they toyed with the letter opener. Long, delicate, silky smooth fingers that would soothe a woman's skin like the touch of a summer breeze. "You've been awfully secretive about what you have—or have not—been up to this past week, you know."

"Have I been? Professional hazard I suppose. Secrets are a way of life in my trade."

Leslie wondered if he had any idea of the phallic significance of the caressing, stroking motions his fingers were making along the length of the letter opener. In a streak of mischief, she started to enlighten him, but then thought better of it. She had a strong feeling that the less said about sublimated sexuality around Michael Bradshaw the better; in any such discussion she was bound to come out the loser.

She said instead, glancing at him with interest, "Are you really a professor?"

"Umm-hmm." The corner of a grin toyed with his mouth. "Does that surprise you?"

She lifted her shoulders negligently. "Does it surprise *you* that I would think twice about believing anything you say? What do you teach?"

"A little number by the name of 'The Influence of Magic, Mysticism and Superstition on American Culture,' among others."

Leslie chuckled. "Now, that *doesn't* surprise me. Sociology department?"

"No, English. I left out part of the course name—'As Seen Through American Literature.' Damn thing's so long I'm always forgetting it."

Now that was interesting. Not that she had given it much thought, but Leslie had never imagined him as an English professor. "How long have you been a part of the academic community?"

"Almost seven years, in and out," he replied, but Leslie almost missed it. Her eyes had happened to stray to his hands again, and as she watched, the sturdy sterling silver began to melt like heated plastic in his hands, curling its gleaming edges around his fingers, molding its once-solid shape into new contours beneath the smooth, dexterous movements of his hands. Her eyes grew wide, a sound caught in her throat, and she stared as the letter opener began to shape itself into a perfect spiral around his index finger.

Just as she was about to gasp a protest or an exclamation, she caught herself. She had seen him do the very same thing on the other side of a two-way mirror less than a week ago and she had almost believed him then, too. It was a trick, an illusion, a silly play for attention, and she was not about to burst into incredulous praise and stunned applause like some besotted groupie.

Firmly, she focused on his face again, and it was as unaffected and as implacable as though he had no expectation of her at all except an easy continuance of their conversation. Very well, two could play at this game. She would just ignore what he was doing—or pretending to do—to her valuable sterling silver letter opener that had been a graduation gift from her aunt ten years ago and had been in *her* family for seventy-five years before that.

She inquired, proud of her pleasant conversational tone, "What made you decide to give up performing?"

He laughed softly, and when he did he tilted his head and the light from the window glinted off his hair magnificently. "Who says I did? I'm a much better actor in front of the classroom than I ever was onstage. It's not easy, you know, to pretend you know everything to a bunch of kids determined to prove you don't know anything. It's the scariest thing I've ever done."

Leslie cast a surreptitious glance at his hands again, and once more he held only a letter opener. She breathed a small, imperceptible sigh of relief. Maybe she had imagined it.

"Anyway," he said, shifting a little in his seat into a more comfortable lounging position, "I came here to find out about what *you* do for a living, not to talk about me. You're supposed to be my liaison, remember? So far I know about everyone's job here but yours."

The slight movement he had made, shifting his crossed ankle a bit higher on his knee, had pulled the fabric tauter around his thigh and drew Leslie's attention unconsciously and inevitably to his lap. Her letter opener was now a small, shiny silver ball, not as large as a golf ball but larger than a walnut, which he massaged absently with the thumb and forefinger of his left hand, the way one would play with a paperweight or test the weight of a nut before it was cracked.

"Umm..." Leslie cleared her throat a little. It was amazing how deadpan he was. And how easily he had managed the maneuver without a shift of a muscle or a change of expression to hint at what he was doing. But that was a magician's art, wasn't it? She was sitting not three feet from him and she hadn't seen a thing. She concentrated on his question. "Mostly I do routine psychological profiles, for the record. I'm afraid I don't make much of a direct contribution at all, although occasionally I'll spot a psychosis that will preclude any real evidence of paranormal phenomena."

"Like what?" he asked curiously.

She shrugged. "Hauntings, mostly. I had one case of a woman who claimed her husband had come back from the grave to kill her—it was pretty dramatic, actually, with a wrecked apartment, threatening notes written in blood on the mirror, a fire, and finally an actual attack with a knife by the supposed ghost—the woman had real wounds. It turned out that she was doing all this to herself to try to expiate some deep-rooted guilt she felt about her husband's death.''

Michael lifted an eyebrow, impressed. "Do you see that kind of thing often?''

"Fortunately, no. Or perhaps unfortunately, because many of the people who come to us voluntarily don't stay long enough for me to do a thorough profile. They feel threatened by the thoroughness of our investigative techniques, and take them for skepticism.'' She shrugged. "There's still the occasional succubus or incubus, which is part of every psychologist's lot, I suppose.'' And she started to explain, "That's—''

"I know.'' The slight crinkling at the corners of Michael's eyes suggested subtle mischief. "A sexual encounter from the spirit world. We should all be so lucky.''

Leslie chuckled. "I suppose it does take some of the messiness out of interpersonal relationships, when your lover is literally not of this world. Anyway, some of the people who come to me with so-called encounters stay for therapy, but most of them insist that what they're experiencing is real and shy away from treatment.''

"They know a good thing when they've got it,'' commented Michael soberly, and Leslie laughed again. He *was* easy to be with.

"So, there you pretty much have it.'' Leslie spread her hands. "My job is to make sure that no psychological detail is overlooked that could explain possible paranormal phenomena by normal means, and to keep thorough, up-to-date case studies that could possibly draw parallels between the lesser-known workings of the human mind and the evidence of paranormal phenomena.''

"In a nutshell.'' Michael grinned, and Leslie smiled back, a little abashed for the professional double-talk.

"Pretty much.''

As they shared that comfortable moment of newly established rapport, which felt so good to Leslie after her initial feelings of wariness and, yes, hostility, around him, her eyes were caught by a glint of silver. This time she almost couldn't maintain her composure. The silver ball, which once had been a letter opener, was now a shimmering stream of mercury that glided back and forth between Michael's cupped hands like an airbrushed rainbow or a child's Slinky toy. It was incredible. It couldn't be, but she was seeing it with her own eyes, a ribbon of silver dancing and glinting in the sunlight, arcing with the absent motion of Michael's hands between one palm and the other.

He was saying, "So what about the Gaynor kids? What have you found out about them?"

Leslie blinked; she looked at him. His expression was casual, his eyes revealing nothing but easy interest, and it struck her suddenly: he didn't realize what he was doing. He wasn't even thinking about it. As some people would drum their fingers absently or make meaningless doodles on a notepad while they talked, Michael Bradshaw occupied his hands with making magic. It came to him as naturally as breathing; it was as unpremeditated as a habit.

Incredible, Leslie thought dully. *Simply incredible.* And there was no longer any point in denying it. She was impressed.

She focused with some difficulty on his question. "What, specifically, do you mean?"

"If you've finished your evaluation, I'd like to see the file," he requested simply.

Abruptly, Leslie's mind returned from things of the netherworld to matters of pragmatism. "I see," she said slowly. "So the Gaynors are to be your first project."

A tilt of his head acknowledged the correctness of her assumption. "That's what I'm here for."

It made sense, of course. The Gaynors were their most important project, their best chance to impress the scientific community—and the federal government—with the accuracy, thoroughness and validity of their work. This case would also, by its very nature, be the perfect testing ground for Michael, and if it passed his test there would be little room for doubt or dispute when the Center brought its report before the public. Leslie couldn't quarrel with the reasons for the assignment, but other, less clear considerations were vying for her attention.

"Let me ask you something, Michael," she said, watching him carefully. "Have you discovered anything this past week, in any of our cases studied, that caused you to suspect fraud?"

"If you mean, have I discovered anything I couldn't explain," he replied frankly, yet with no show of concern, "the answer is no. I can duplicate or delineate everything I've seen here so far. But that doesn't mean..." He lifted a warning finger to forestall her objection. Leslie resisted the impulse to look and see what had become of the letter opener. "That I'm throwing the whole thing out as bogus. I promised to keep an open mind, remember?" The hint of a relaxed, teasing grin was in his eyes. "Right now I'm only interested in the Gaynors, and believe me, I have no intention of making snap judgments with you riding shotgun. But in order to make any kind of judgment at all I have to have the whole picture. So I need your files."

Therein lay the problem. She was a research specialist, but she was still a doctor. There was the small matter of patient-doctor confidentiality, even though the Gaynors were not exactly patients. Michael was not a doctor, or even a scientist. He wasn't even, technically, a part of the research team; he was only a consultant. She thought perhaps if it had been any other case the question of ethics would not have been so severe, but she couldn't help being a little protective of the twins. She had to be cautious.

And she had to be firm.

"I can't give you the file, Michael," she said.

Something crossed his eyes—a shadow, a question, or merely an instinctive reaction to her breech of the tenuous trust that had begun to build between them. But it was gone almost immediately, and he merely inquired mildly, "Do you mind telling me why?"

She knew resistance was as futile as her reasons were vague. If Michael wanted the Gaynor file he could take it just as easily as he had taken her car keys, and that was only one of the reasons why she didn't want to give it to him. But she said firmly, "They're my patients, and there's a question of ethics. You're not a professional—"

"I thought we had agreed to cooperate."

"I think you should be able to reach your own conclusions without the prejudice of my opinion. You are, after all, involved in the technical end of the research, and the intellectual and emotional status of the subjects shouldn't have anything to do with—"

"In other words, you don't trust me to use the information objectively." His voice was mild, and his face frustratingly unreadable.

Leslie swallowed uncomfortably. "It's a bit more complicated than that." Oh, yes, quite a bit. He was asking her to aid and abet him in the abortion of this project, and the Gaynors represented too much of a challenge, too many possibilities for her to stand by and see their case dismissed before they had even begun to investigate. No doubt he would reach whatever conclusions he intended to reach with or without her help, but she simply could not take an active part in assisting him. Too much was at stake.

And, yes, the bottom line was she didn't trust him. He had promised to be open-minded; she didn't believe him. He had promised to look only for the truth, but how could she believe him when he had made his position on what they did here so abundantly clear, when she had been sitting here and watching him manipulate reality between his quick, lithe fingers for the past quarter of an hour?

Even as she realized this, her hand went surreptitiously, protectively, to the drawer that guarded the file. His quick eyes noticed the movement, and registered it with a gentle clicking of his tongue. "Shame on you, Dr. Roarke. I would never use my powers of prestidigitation to take from you what you didn't want to give. That—'' he lifted an eyebrow meaningfully ''—would be unethical.''

''You did it with my car keys,'' she pointed out, embarrassed to be caught in her suspicions and instantly defensive. ''And you did it to enter my house without my permission.''

''Two entirely different matters,'' he said, dismissing her airily. The man was impossible to ruffle. ''You see, you wanted me to do those things, whether you realize it or not.''

''I think you have a very twisted sense of ethics,'' Leslie muttered, and because it looked foolish not to do so, she removed her hand from the drawer after a brief glance to make sure the file was still there.

He fastened her with an unexpectedly curious, uncomfortably penetrating look. ''Don't you believe in *anything*, Dr. Leslie Roarke?'' he inquired with a mild puzzlement that was at once both intimidating and disarming.

Leslie moved her eyes meaningfully to his hands. He didn't seem to notice. The letter opener had now become a perfectly forged heart, which he twirled absently around his index finger. Leslie looked back at him. She replied evenly, ''And just what am I supposed to believe in?''

The definitive lines of his sharp, alert face relaxed into a wonderfully sensuous, vaguely teasing smile. ''Me, for a start.''

Leslie's own smile was mirthless, superior and knowledgeable. ''Oh, I'm sure you'd like that, Mr. Bradshaw.'' She extended her hand deliberately for her letter opener— or what was left of it.

Michael looked puzzled for a minute, and then glanced down at what he held. ''Oh, sorry,'' he murmured, and handed it to her. It was once again nothing more than a sterling silver letter opener, heavy and solid, slightly smudged with his fingerprints, but without a crease or a scratch.

Her telephone buzzed, and she reached for it. Michael

got lazily to his feet as she spoke into the receiver, her eyes still fixed with some fascination on the letter opener.

"We'll finish this conversation later," he promised, starting toward the door, and Leslie couldn't stand it any longer. She had to know.

"Wait a minute," she said, and put her caller unceremoniously on hold. Michael turned.

Leslie picked up the letter opener, pointing it in his direction. She knew if she didn't confront him with it the unanswered question would bother her the rest of the day. "Will you tell me please—just to satisfy my own curiosity—how you did that?"

He looked innocent. "Did what?"

Leslie gave an impatient, frustrated grimace. "Don't be coy. The letter opener. Did you have the props in your pockets, up your sleeves? How could you have made them look so much like my letter opener? Did you remember it from the last time you were here and design your props after it? What a silly thing to do! Just tell me how you did it, that's all."

He looked thoughtful for a moment, and then decided, seriously, "No."

She gave him a half-belligerent, half-incredulous look. "Why not?"

"Because," he responded, and he winked at her as he reached for the doorknob, "some things just have to be accepted on faith."

Chapter Six

The building did not have central air and toward the late afternoon the sticky heat began to gather even in Leslie's relatively well-shaded lower-floor office. She had removed her lab coat and pushed up the sleeves on her crepe blouse, and she could feel her hair beginning to wilt.

She was spending more time at the Center than she normally did, and there was no question about it—the reason was Michael Bradshaw. She was by no means neglecting her work at the children's hospital, but she found herself working longer hours so that she might spend as much time at the Center as possible. She told herself the reason for that was a very reasonable need to keep an eye on Michael as the Center underwent this most important crisis of its life, and it was, in part, true. But equally as important, if she was honest with herself, was the simple need to keep an eye on Michael Bradshaw.

She had an appointment that afternoon with one of her favorite—and most challenging—patients from the children's hospital, and she was hurriedly returning some borrowed videotapes of the Gaynor twins to the storage room before she left the Center for the day. The video-storage room was little more than a small closet—perhaps designed as a servant's pantry at one time—and one of the coolest places the building had to offer. She was perched atop a small stepladder, filing a tape on the top shelf, when she sensed the presence behind her. She did not have to turn around to know who it was.

Michael stood there for a moment, observing with an unexpected sense of pleasure the way her ponytail curled at the ends, precisely at the midpoint of her shoulder blades, and brushed the silky fabric of her beige blouse. He had thought the ponytail severe and unflattering when he had seen her this morning; from the back it looked girlish, and in some inexplicable way, appealing. The rolled-up sleeves of her blouse gave him his first glimpse of pretty wrists and forearms and he wondered in amusement how it could be that he was so dangerously close to becoming obsessed with a woman whose elbows he had not even seen yet. The pale linen slacks fell in a smooth line over her small hips and thighs, straight over her ankles to the edges of low-heeled shoes. What a very precise woman was his Dr. Roarke. Never rumpled, never rattled, never discomposed. All of which, of course, made imagining the moment when she would become all of those things for him all the more exciting.

She said, without turning around, "What do you want?"

Michael laughed softly and stepped inside. As he did, his foot brushed against the heavy door and it swung closed behind him. "You're always asking me that," he pointed out.

Leslie gave an annoyed glance at the closed door and calmly replaced the last tape. She could feel Michael's eyes on her backside as she bent to file the tape on the third shelf and then climbed down from the stepladder. "That's because you're always sneaking up on me."

Again he chuckled. His pale eyes took on a very unsettling spark in the light from the bare overhead bulb. "I don't think you've ever been 'sneaked up on' in your life, Dr. Roarke. You are the most impossible person to startle I've ever met."

She smiled at him sweetly. "One learns to be prepared for the unexpected in this business, Mr. Bradshaw." She had never realized just *how* small this closet was before.

She would have to brush up against him to get past, and even then it could not be accomplished without a great deal of shifting of arms and legs and hips, unless he decided to take the hint and precede her.

Leslie waited, impatiently, for him to do just that, but he seemed in no particular hurry to leave. He just stood there with his supple, lounging grace, taking up most of the space and a great deal of the air, looking at her. "Did you come in here for something in particular?" she said.

Michael smiled. "A couple of things, actually. I need a tape." And he nodded to the shelf that her shoulders blocked. "Number fifty-two. Would you mind?"

Leslie turned to retrieve the tape, but it was not in its slot. In its place lay a single yellow rose—which, needless to say, had not been there thirty seconds ago when she had climbed down from the stepladder. She lifted it slowly, half expecting it to disappear in her hands, and lifted it to her face. It was fragrant, as soft as velvet and still moist with dew. The part of her that should have been annoyed with his perplexing sleight of hand instead unexpectedly softened, and she felt a smile curve her lips as she inhaled the wonderful scent. Yellow roses were her favorites. No one had ever known that; no one had ever cared enough to inquire; no one had ever given them to her before.

Ah, damn it, Michael, she thought, helpless with resignation. *Just when I think I could stay permanently suspicious of you, you have to go and do something like this.* It was silly, of course, to be so touched by a simple gift, a careless trick, but when gifts are so rare in one's life even the smallest one can take on enormous significance.

She didn't realize she was still smiling until she looked up and saw the tenderness of her smile reflected in Michael's eyes. "You look so lovely when you smile like that," he said softly. "Vulnerable. Almost touchable. That's a good thing, Leslie."

But it was not, Leslie knew immediately. Not now, not in this place, not with him. Not when they were so close that, standing on opposite sides of the room, their breath mingled and the fragrance of the rose combined with that gentle spicy scent of his like an aphrodisiac. She glanced quickly down at the flower again, just for the moment it took to reorient herself, and she inquired casually, "Where did you get it?"

"If I told you that, it would take all the romance away, wouldn't it?"

"Not really," she argued logically. "A rose would smell just as sweet whether it came from the florist's shop in town or out of your back garden. I was just curious, that's all."

His eyes crinkled with subtle dancing lights, and there was affectionate amusement in his voice. "How immanently practical of you, Dr. Roarke. And, as always, how insufferably logical. Besides being impossible to startle, you are almost the most annoyingly difficult woman to impress I've ever met."

"Ah, well, Mr. Bradshaw," she replied lightly, reaching for the door. "I'm sure we can all use a challenge now and then."

He blocked her way, as she knew he would. Rather than duck under his arm or squeeze her body past his to open the door, she paused to look up at him politely. "Was there anything else you wanted?"

"Just one more thing, really." He looked down at her, quite seriously, rather thoughtfully and announced mildly, "I've decided I want to be your lover."

For just the briefest half-second Michael had the satisfaction of seeing her look startled. And as thought completely fled Leslie in the lurch of a heartbeat, she cast about the small, cramped room and all she could manage to say was, "Here?"

His laughter was low and gentle and as entrancing as a mountain brook. It filled his eyes, his face, the whole room. His hands dropped lightly to her shoulders and he replied, "If here is my only choice, it will do as well as any other place, I suppose."

Leslie felt the heat rush, not creep, out of her collar and over her face in an explosion of graceless discomfiture—

she, who had forgotten how to blush more years ago than she cared to count, and whose quick mind had a store of calculated quips lying in wait for just such an occasion as this; she whose very life's work depended on her never being caught off guard....

She twisted away from his light embrace and reached for the doorknob. It did not budge. She twisted again, putting some of her weight against the door, and Michael obligingly stepped back a fraction to allow her access. In a moment she straightened up, swallowed hard, and turned to face him with as much composure as was humanly possible. "Very clever, Mr. Bradshaw," she said stiffly. "Now will you kindly unlock the door? It's getting stuffy in here."

"Yes, it is, isn't it?" he agreed pleasantly. "Is the door locked?"

"You know damn well it is." She kept her voice very even. "You locked it."

He lifted an affronted eyebrow. "My dear Dr. Roarke, I did no such thing. I don't even have a key."

Leslie leaned flat against the door, meeting his amused gaze with ice in her own. "All right, Michael. You've had your little joke. Now will you kindly tell me what you want from me so that we can both get back to work?"

"I believe I already told you that." He moved toward her—moved, perhaps, was not even the word; glided, more likely, or leaned—and placed his hands on either side of her shoulders, bracing his palms against the doorframe behind her. He didn't touch her, not at any point, but his body was covering hers in warmth and scent and electric presence; the sensation of it was like a low thrumming that began somewhere deep within her circulatory system and spread slowly outward to her veins. She felt enfolded by him.

Leslie met those most disturbing sensations with determination in her eyes and firmness in her voice as she informed him, "This is spiteful, childish, and very unworthy of you. If you think for one minute that I'm going to put up with—''

His lips captured hers with a single graceful movement that took no more than a breath, and because of its very swiftness caught Leslie completely off guard. One moment he was leaning above her with teasing in his eyes and the next his lips were taking hers, and it was not that Leslie had not expected it to happen—she simply had not expected it to be like this.

The gentleness of the assault was what surprised her. A soft, warm, moist invasion that flowed into her senses and blended with them, meeting not a moment's resistance or protest. He kissed her, simply kissed her, tilting his head slightly to better taste her, to more thoroughly caress her, and not until his tongue penetrated the inner recesses of her mouth did she realize she had responded with lips parted and welcoming, for in truth, she was helpless to do anything else.

He drew her against him; dimly she felt his indrawn breath with the shock that went through both of them at this symbolic joining of their bodies. Her arms were around his neck, the yellow rose dangling limply from one hand, and she tasted him inside her, dark and tangy with that peculiar sweet sharp scent that was all his own. The pores of her skin opened to a rush of heat, and she could feel her heart beat wild and heavy and from somewhere deep within her drugged consciousness was the vagrant thought, *God, this is wonderful. He is wonderful.* Just as she had always known it would be.

He drew her in, tasting her with leisurely exploration, making her a part of him, and it was stunning what he did to her. Her skin tingled and prickled with an electric charge that was maddening; her muscles lost their tensile ability; and she thought the dizziness that swam about her was only from the slowly mounting difficulty she had drawing breath. She lost herself, her reason, her ability to distinguish reality, and she thought that if this was an illusion it was his greatest one yet.

So completely wrapped up in him, so completely a part of him, was she that she hardly realized when he had ceased to kiss her and simply held her, pliant and helpless, against his chest. Gradually she became aware that the roaring in her ears was the sound of his deep, uneven breath, and the rapid thud and counter-thud against her rib cage was his heartbeat as well as hers. She felt weak, heavy-limbed, every nerve ending awakened and alive, and for the moment she had neither the will nor the energy to step away.

His hand lifted to caress her hair, brushing lightly over her shoulder. The rise and fall of his chest was slow and heavy against her breasts, and when he bent to touch his lips to her cheek she shivered. He whispered huskily, "Do you feel that, Leslie? Do you feel it between us? That's magic."

His fingertips gilded down the upper curve of her arm, which was still looped around his neck, and then down the side of her torso, barely teasing the shape of her firm, uplifted breast, downward to her waist, and then up again. She knew she must step away. She said, surprised at the throaty tenor of her own voice, "The first kiss is always exciting." With all the strength of will she possessed, she loosened her arms from his neck, but there was no place to step to. Her back was against the door. "It's adrenaline," she explained, "and hormones."

He smiled, and his eyes were bright and dark at the same time, lit with an inner heat that was powerful and hypnotic. Just looking at him, Leslie felt her throat grow dry. Still, she had not quite managed to get her breathing back to normal.

"And the second kiss?" he asked, those burning eyes moving downward to her lips, "is it just as exciting?"

I don't see how it possibly could be, Leslie thought helplessly, and stammered, "Actually, once the newness has worn off... Michael, I—I don't think we—"

His hands took her face; he covered her mouth with his, and this time it was a hungry, demanding kiss that gave vent to the urgency that had been restrained before, and with a sudden and brief-lived clarity of reason Leslie realized that this was no illusion. The need she could taste within him was as real and as demanding and as debilitating as her own. There was nothing contrived or designed about what was flaring between them; each was its victim as much as its creator, and though the knowledge was frightening it was also exhilarating.

He devoured her; he consumed her; he overpowered her senses. He made her breasts ache and her legs weaken and her womb tighten in anticipation of him. She never felt the button being loosened, never noticed his movement, but somehow his hands were inside the waistband of her slacks, sliding over the slope of her hips, beneath the fabric of her bikini panties, and her breath stopped; her heart stopped and everything within her flared in an acute and sense-robbing awareness as she felt those long, strong fingers against her bare skin, curling intimately around her buttocks.

He groaned low in his throat, a wonderfully vulnerable and helpless sound that was lost within the recesses of her mouth as he pulled her close to him, his hands pressing against her nakedness, his hardness against the soft, yearning flesh of her abdomen. Something wild and untamed surged through her and was reflected back from him and she thought, with her last shred of conscious reason, *If we don't stop soon, it will be too late.* But she didn't try to summon the will to do anything about it. She wasn't, at that moment, certain she wanted to.

And then, just as swiftly as it had begun, it was over. His hands were light upon her waist, his mouth moved away from hers, and he was looking down into her flushed, heated face with dampness and tightness upon his own and he smiled, almost. "I don't know about you," he said, "but I found that pretty exciting."

He controlled his breathing with a remarkable effort Leslie could sense, but he could do nothing about the dark fever in his eyes. Leslie, dazed and shaken, still aching from the loss of contact, thought, *Another minute. Another minute and we would have made love here on the dusty floor of this closet and I wouldn't have minded, wouldn't have protested.... Damn you Michael, how did you do that to me?*

And then swiftly, as though taking the very thoughts from her head, his hands tightened upon her waist; the playful smile he had tried to force onto his lips was wiped away as though it had never been, and his eyes went to hers with a dark intensity that was almost palpable. "Come home with me, Leslie," he said in a low voice. "Let's make love to each other...."

Her lips, stung and swollen and aching for the taste of him, parted for a reply. *Think, Leslie.* She took a breath. *You know better than this, Leslie.* Another breath. His eyes searched hers hungrily, commandingly. *You don't need this, Leslie.* She took another breath. She met his eyes evenly. *That's better.* She said, "No, Michael."

He didn't release her, either with his hands or his eyes. He inquired gently, "Why not?"

"Because," she replied simply, feeling better now, slowly regaining control, "I don't go to bed with everyone I meet."

There was a flicker of something deep within his eyes—hurt, or disappointment—that made her instantly defensive. But what did he expect her to say? What did he expect her to do? Five minutes in a musty closet with him and she was supposed to surrender to him body and soul? A kiss was a kiss but she had no intention of becoming involved with this man.

He smiled. "Actually," he replied, his thumbs massaging a light and sensuous pattern against her rib cage, "neither do I. But would you care to be more specific?"

What an entrancing smile he had. What magical hands. And how Leslie's own hands ached to return his caresses. She kept her arms deliberately at her sides. The yellow rose, crushed at some point during their embrace, released a potent and drugging perfume into the small confines. She said, swallowing hard, "Will you—Will you stop touching me please?"

After only a moment's pause he dropped his hands, and the tender affection of understanding in his eyes was almost her undoing. "Only because I do want to hear your answer to this one, Dr. Roarke," he answered quietly. Without her having to ask, he took a step backward, freeing her at last to breathe properly.

Leslie drew in a deep breath of warm air scented with roses and Michael; she felt her pulses begin to slow fractionally and the strange shivery feeling in her muscles begin to dissipate. She knew it was best to get it out in the open, for he was persistent and her will, which she had heretofore always thought of as iron, had just been proven to be strangely malleable at his hands. And Leslie had no room in her life for a mistake as big as the one she had almost made with him.

"We're not going to have an affair, Michael."

He smiled, a delighted, relaxed spark dancing in his eyes. "I love it when you get firm and businesslike. I don't want to have an affair with you. I want to have a relatively lengthy and possibly even meaningful relationship with you."

Her chin jutted a fraction higher, her kiss-rouged lips compressed sternly. "Men," she said disdainfully. "You're always thinking with your hormones." She turned toward the door. "We can either talk about this when you're ready to be serious or forget it completely, and if you're interested in my opinion I'd prefer the latter. Will you let me leave now?"

He reached out a hand to stay her, but dropped it immediately when the electricity of his touch caused her to start unexpectedly and recoil from him. Sexual nerve endings were still aflame and she wasn't nearly as in control as she wished to appear. It was to Michael's credit that he didn't press the advantage he could so clearly see.

"For your information," he said quietly, "I was serious." And then a slight puzzlement laced the intensely interested look in his eyes as he inquired, "What is it about you, Leslie, that makes you so unwilling to believe a man could care for you?"

Leslie felt a prickling in her throat that registered objection to so close a truth—and one he had no right to guess. But her gaze was unwavering and her demeanor calm as she replied, "It has nothing to do with men in general, Michael."

"Like hell it doesn't." But his voice was gentle and perceptive. "You told me yourself you intimidate men. That doesn't happen by accident, Les, you do it on purpose. To defend yourself. Does it bother you that you've found one man you can't intimidate?"

She released a long-suffering sigh. "There you go again, playing psychologist."

The upward turn of a corner of his lips was wonderfully relaxed, and relaxing. "Half of magic is in the mind, you know. Amateur psychology is my stock in trade."

She looked at him, feeling the warmth and easy companionability that radiated from him subtly alter the mood of the close little room from almost unbearable tension to friendliness and humor. And she couldn't help it; she found herself smiling back. He was so easy to like. So damned impossible to stay annoyed with.

"Michael," she insisted gently, "use your common sense. We're both too mature to start something that we know from the beginning is going to be bad for both of us. We have to work together. Worse yet, we're working on opposite sides of the field. A personal involvement would just make things messy; you know that. We have to stay objective."

He looked at her thoughtfully. When he spoke, his voice was serious, and so was his expression. "We're going to be working together all summer, Leslie. I don't think either of us can wait that long."

Leslie swallowed because that prickling had begun in her throat again, and she had to move her eyes away quickly, to a high shelf over his shoulder, before he read acknowledgment of that very acute truth in her eyes.

"Let's go, Michael. I have an appointment at the hospital and I'm going to be late."

"I'll go with you," he volunteered.

"Don't be ridiculous."

"I want to spend the afternoon with you."

"I don't allow bystanders to sightsee at my private therapy sessions." As she spoke, she was busily fumbling with the doorknob. It still wouldn't budge. And she knew that things were far from settled between them.

She felt his closeness like the brush of wings. He touched her lightly—or perhaps not at all—and her breath stopped. Her hand went limp on the doorknob. Helplessly she was turned toward him and she never knew whether it was through his power or her own.

His eyes were as soft and as opalescent as twin moons, his fingertips light as he brushed back a strand of hair that had come loose from her ponytail. And he said, "Do you know what I think? I think it doesn't have much at all to do with whether or not we're working together or what side of the argument we're on. I think it has to do with trusting, and knowing, and letting go enough to believe in something outside yourself for once. In other words, being in love." He smiled. He was a mesmerist when he smiled, robbing her of her will, her reason, her conscious thought. "And that's okay with me," he decided. "Because I think I'd like to fall in love with you, too."

She laughed nervously, because that was the only possible response to such an incredible statement, and because that was the only way she knew to break the spell he was exerting over her so subtly, so powerfully. "Simply getting me into bed would be a lot easier," she informed him, "because it would take a minor miracle to make me fall in love with you."

His planed, enigmatic face relaxed, the way she loved to see it; his eyes crinkled, ever so slightly, at the corners. "Oh, is that all?" he replied easily, and let his hands drop from the caressing motions he was making around her face. "Minor miracles are no problem for me. It's the major ones that take a little longer."

She knew, with a sudden and intense certainty, that he was speaking nothing more than the truth. This man, who bent the impossible to his will with careless effort, who plucked flowers out of the air and turned silver into mercury and controlled the rhythm of her heart with a single look, this man could overcome a lifetime of caution and restraint in the time it takes to draw a breath, and without giving the matter more than a second's thought. He could take her carefully ordered life and turn it into chaos; he could take her well-formed concept of herself and turn it inside out; he could leave her shattered and aching and bewildered, for she knew that once she let Michael Bradshaw into her life nothing would ever be the same again.

She said, keeping her voice firm. "Let me go now, Michael. I'm late."

He stepped away from her, and the look in his eyes caused her a moment of confusion. It was perception mixed with tenderness and, strangely enough, something that looked like sympathy. It was the look one would give a child who had been inadvertently frightened by a well-meant surprise. He said gently, "The door is unlocked, Leslie." And he added with a slight softening of his features she could not begin to understand, "It always was."

She tried the doorknob, and he was right. The door opened easily, and she walked through it without looking back.

Chapter Seven

Tony Swan was eight years old. He loved television—especially movies—classical music, the color blue, and anything with which he could make loud, arrhythmic, ear-splitting noises. He was terrified of blinking lights, spinning tops and spiral notebooks. Like so many autistic children, Tony possessed an almost mystical beauty: gentle, perfectly formed features, dark hair, and huge dark eyes that seemed to hold the secrets of the universe in their depths.

His mother called him her "miracle child," and in many ways that was precisely what he was. There was no precise psychological definition of the type of intelligence Tony displayed. He couldn't read or write, but his photographic memory could spot a picture that was hanging half a millimeter off center or a sofa cushion that was only slightly rearranged since the last time he had seen a room, and his frustration level rose steadily until the detail was corrected. His speech had never progressed beyond baby babble—and was always rendered at a high, intense level approaching a scream—but he could sing an entire aria without missing a note after having heard it only once. He could solve complex geometric and mathematical puzzles using blocks and cutouts, but he could not recognize number symbols. Tony Swan had quickly taught Leslie to discard everything she had ever known about using "normalcy" as a standard by which to measure the capacity of the human mind. Tony was not ordinary, but Leslie sometimes wondered whether she—or indeed anyone—had the right to make empirical judgments based on the scant information available about the working of a mind like Tony's.

Tony sat on the floor of Leslie's office, his legs crossed, slowly rocking back and forth. He was staring soberly at his latest creation: concentric circles of dominos arranged in descending numerical order, sixes forming the outer circle and containing exactly six dominos, five dominos each with five dots forming a circle inside the sixes, and so on until the single domino displaying a single dot sat at the center of the circle. Leslie knew that if she took a calibrated measuring device and applied it to the circle she would find that each one measured precisely three-hundred-sixty degrees and that the distance between each rectangular block in each circle would not vary by a fraction. If she had stayed up all night, with a slide rule, she would not have been able to manage such a feat; Tony had accomplished it in less than ten minutes.

His mother, sitting across the desk from Leslie, cast an affectionate look toward her son. "I know it must be hard for you to imagine, Dr. Roarke, but he's like a different child from the little boy we first brought here two years ago. I was thinking about it just yesterday when we went shopping. I couldn't have taken him to the mailbox two years ago, much less to a crowded supermarket." Mrs. Swan flashed her a grin. "I'm almost ready to tackle the mall."

Leslie smiled. "I think we may have to work up to that." Tony was very sensitive to visual stimulation, and most especially to disorder. The movement and chaos of crowds tended to invoke hysteria. "And how was he at the supermarket?"

"Only one episode," Mrs. Swan replied cheerfully, "when we were getting ready to leave. I think twenty minutes is about his limit, and then the cash registers seemed to set him off."

Leslie felt a brief moment of sympathy for the woman

who had to arrange her life around such eccentricities—to whom even twenty minutes in the grocery store with her son was a bonus for which to be grateful.

Leslie nodded. "He is making progress. I thought that supermarkets would be the best place to start—there's a mathematical precision about the way shelves are arranged in a grocery store that you won't find anywhere else." She grinned. "Some marketing genius figured out a long time ago that when people enter a supermarket the quickest way to their pocketbooks is through the subconscious mind. In that way we're not so different from Tony as we might think."

"Well, I want to thank you," Mrs. Swan said sincerely. "Since he's been with you I really think Tony has made faster progress than ever before."

Leslie had only had Tony in therapy for three months, as part of a caseload transfer when his former doctor went into private practice in another state. The change had been traumatic at first, but once she had gained Tony's trust, his therapy had proceeded well. She only wished she had worked with him from the beginning. There was so much about him she didn't know—despite his previous doctor's impeccable records and frequent telephone consultations—things that she must discover for herself and that would take years to learn.

She replied, "Most of the credit belongs to Tony. He's quite a young man."

"Sometimes I almost think there's a chance after all, for Tony to lead a normal life...." But the other woman stopped when she saw the familiar warning of reproach in Leslie's eyes.

"I thought we'd all agreed not to wait for miracles, Mrs. Swan," Leslie reminded her gently. "The only way either Tony or your family is ever going to find any kind of happiness is to deal with reality the way you find it."

"But you said yourself that if we could make a breakthrough in his speech—"

"That's right," agreed Leslie. "I think if Tony was able

to communicate with us, his frustration would be decreased enormously, and it would be the first step toward teaching him to live in our world, instead of his own. But we both know that such a breakthrough is a long way off.'' She didn't add, as she probably should have, that it was virtually impossible. Tony's speech pathology, as she had tried to make his parents understand, was not a separate entity unto itself but an integral part of his entire disorder. The symptom could not be treated unless the syndrome was also cured.

For a moment the optimism in Mrs. Swan's eyes faltered, but then reasserted itself. ''Well,'' she insisted cheerfully, ''they say Einstein was autistic, and he didn't do so badly, did he?''

Leslie smiled. ''They'' said a lot of things about Einstein, and as long as believing the myth kept Mrs. Swan's spirits up, Leslie was not about to disillusion her.

Mrs. Swan cast another glance at her son; her hands tightened about her purse as though in preparation for leaving, and then she gave Leslie a suddenly shy look. ''Dr. Roarke...you don't know how I hate to ask you this...but I was wondering... Well...'' She looked down at her hands, took a breath, and faced Leslie again with reluctance and embarrassment in her eyes. ''My husband and I have been invited to a company picnic tomorrow and you know I wouldn't even consider going, but Tony has been doing so much better. And it's been—well, years, since Jack and I went anywhere together, and sometimes it *is* hard.... You're the only one I really trust with Tony,'' she blurted suddenly, ''and I was wondering if—tomorrow—you might take him for a while?''

Leslie immediately saw by the slight hint of desperation in the other woman's eyes that, however nicely Tony might be progressing, she was not handling the strain of caring for a mentally handicapped child nearly as well as she pretended. Leslie met that realization with a small stab of frustration mixed with genuine sympathy. She had made it clear from the beginning that Tony was not entering into therapy alone—this was a family matter and Leslie was tendering services to them as a family unit. Why, then, for heaven's sake, couldn't the Swans be honest with her about the problems they were having? How could she be expected to help them if they persisted in playing martyrs?

Mrs. Swan insisted, "We wouldn't stay long—I mean, it wouldn't be an all-day, all-night affair...."

Leslie held up a hand, mildly. She did not want to encourage the Swan's to become dependent on her, for babysitting or anything else, but it wasn't as though she hadn't done this sort of thing before. When Tony had first come under her care she had taken him home for three weekends in a row, knowing that was the fastest way to build up trust between them, and he would feel secure with her in a way he would not with anyone else at this point. On the other hand Leslie did not wish to jeopardize all the progress they had made recently by leaving him in the hands of a stranger.

She said, "Of course I'll be glad to have him. You know that I want you and your husband to see to your own needs first; we've discussed that many times. We've also discussed..." And now a look of gentle reprimand came into her eyes. "Your hiring a housekeeper, someone who can be introduced to Tony gradually and accepted as part of the family, someone who can free you from some of the responsibility of caring for him."

Mrs. Swan looked abashed. "I know. I—I just haven't seemed to find the time to interview anyone."

Typically, she didn't want to relinquish the control and the authority she had had over her son all his life. Though she could see what the stress was doing to her, she couldn't let go of the responsibility. Leslie knew that they still had a lot of work to do on that problem before she could consider Mrs. Swan's emotional health stable.

She said, "As I said, I'll be glad to have Tony tomorrow, and I want you and your husband to stay as long as you like. He can even spend the night, if it would help. But next session," she reminded her sternly, "we're going to do a lot of talking about your finding a housekeeper."

Relief flooded Mrs. Swan's face as she got to her feet. "You don't know how much we appreciate this. We won't stay away long, I promise. And I'll bring Tony right here to the office tomorrow morning—about ten?" She waited for Leslie's nod, and then continued quickly, "And we'll pick him up back here at five—if that's not too late."

"That will be fine," Leslie assured her, thinking that she and Tony could use the time to work on the new program she had devised regarding spatial relationships.

Mrs. Swan approached her son gently. "It's time to go now, Tony. Say goodbye to Dr. Roarke."

Tony rocked back and forth, lost in his own world, reminding Leslie of a primitive medicine man worshiping before a shrine of such architectural complexity that archaeologists would still be wondering, centuries later, how savages could have created such a marvel. The parallel made her smile, and when Tony's mother touched his arm he came back to earth with a start, letting forth a stream of assertive gibberish that made both women wince after such a long and peaceful silence.

Leslie got up and came around the desk, bending before Tony. "I'll see you tomorrow, Tony. You're coming to my house."

There was absolutely no sign of comprehension in Tony's eyes, though it was a known fact that he understood more than half of what was being said to him. He returned something totally incomprehensible at the top of his lungs.

Leslie smiled at his mother. "I'll see you here tomorrow. And try to relax and have fun. Tony will be fine with me and you and your husband deserve a day off."

The other woman smiled her thanks and led Tony, still shouting, out of the office.

Silence echoed when he was gone and Leslie resumed her seat behind her desk, releasing a small sigh of disappointment, not relief. She had gone immediately from Michael to the hospital, and for the past four hours she had been so busy she hadn't had a chance to think. Now that her last patient was gone, there was nothing to keep her restless thoughts from turning back to Michael.

I've decided I want to be your lover. What an incredible thing to say, and it made her skin tingle and her heartbeat grow faster just thinking about it. Sometimes subtlety was the most potent aphrodisiac; sometimes sheer bluntness had a more erotic power than all the whispered words and sultry looks in the world. Michael, somehow, had managed to master both techniques.

The yellow rose, a little bruised and crumpled but basically none the worse for wear, sat in a small bud vase in the center of her desk and now she reached out to stroke its misty petals, smiling a little. She could no more explain how he had pulled that flower out of thin air than she could understand how he had reduced her to a composite of shivering nerve endings with nothing more than a kiss, a kiss much like the one millions of men gave to millions of women every day; a kiss, in its technical expertise, not unlike many others she had known in her lifetime, but with an effect so vastly different it was almost incomprehensible. And perhaps Michael was right about one thing, at least. Understanding might, indeed, take the romance away, and for the first time in her life she wasn't at all sure that would be a good thing.

Ah, hell, she thought sourly, propping her hand on her chin and looking for all the world like a wistful child as she gazed out the window. *Why do complications come along when you're least prepared for them?*

Under other circumstances she would have been more than happy to have a brief, careless affair with Michael Bradshaw. It was useless to pretend the sexual chemistry wasn't there; it had been sparkling like quicksilver between them since the moment he walked into her office, and the stunning culmination to which it had built by this afternoon was only to be expected. Oh, yes, going to bed with him would hardly be the most disastrous thing that had ever happened in her life. Sex with Michael would be wonderful. Intimacy with him would be impossible.

He was in all ways so completely opposite from everything she valued and respected—in fact, everything she *was*—that a mutual meeting ground between them was nonexistent. He was quick, smooth talking and playful, where she was pedantic, careful and studious. To him life was a game—to her life, with all its intricacies and complexities, was a vocation, an almost sacred calling. She didn't like his arrogance or his self-assurance when it came to manipulating others. But most important of all was the small matter of trust. How could she ever trust a man who had spent half his life perfecting the art of deception?

The late afternoon sun sparkled off the pristine white sidewalks and colorful beds of geraniums like mirrors on the water, reminding her unexpectedly of Michael's eyes, which made her think what a perfect day this would be for sailing. The water would be glinting golden with the day's last rays, swelling every now and again with gentle silver-green waves; the gulls, as white as starched handkerchiefs against the sky, would be cawing and careening overhead and the salt spray would taste like kisses....

She thought absently about taking Tony to the beach tomorrow. It would be an adventure, and she thought he was ready for the challenge. He did love the water, and perhaps if they could find a quiet cove somewhere without too many people and too much noise...

She thought about Michael at the stern of a boat, the sun catching the golden hairs on his taut, muscled legs, his strong fingers wrapped around a guy rope, his smooth face narrowed with concentration. She wondered again how he had done that illusion with the letter opener. Winston had said Michael was the best in the world.

She scowled a little as she brought herself back to the present, packing up her briefcase to go home. Understanding people was her life's calling; she made a living out of answering unanswerable questions, and that, she knew, was the most frustrating thing of all. She might very well intimidate men, and perhaps that did not make for a very romantic or long-term relationship, but at least she always understood them. She could never consider taking as a lover a man who was as much a puzzle to her as...well, as that silly rose he had conjured out of thin air. She could not deal with mysteries, and nothing solid could be built on uncertainty.

She left the hospital resolved to put the minor flirtation with Michael Bradshaw out of her mind but that, like so many other things in life, was much easier said than done.

AS HE DID EVERY EVENING, Michael sat on deck at sunset, feeling the breeze in his hair and the taste of the sea in his mouth, listening to the sound of the boats returning from their day's excursions, the gulls fighting with fishermen over the catch. At his side was a frosted glass of orange juice, and his hands absently manipulated a deck of playing cards.

He fanned the cards out on a small table before him, fifty-two cards, thirteen of each suit. With a motion as quick and as subtle as a heartbeat, he closed the deck, tapped it, and fanned it again. Fifty-two cards, all jack of spades. He shuffled the cards, his scowl distant and preoccupied. He was thinking about Leslie, and wishing there was something stronger than juice in that tumbler.

Had he really said that to her? *Lengthy and possibly even meaningful relationship...* Who was he kidding? He had never said that to a woman in his life. He, who took such scrupulous care to be straightforward in his personal life, who prized honesty above all things. He couldn't believe those words had come out of his mouth.

The cards whirred under the skillful manipulations of his fingers. Fifty-two red cards; fifty-two black. Alternating red and black. Fifty-two clubs; shuffle, cut, fifty-two blank cards.

He remembered how she had looked when he gave her the flower. It seemed as though he'd waited half his life to see that look. Misty, vulnerable, shyly grateful... And then so quickly covered that he would have gladly filled the room with yellow roses just to get one more glimpse of that girlish joy in her eyes. He might yet do it.

He set the deck on the table and began to methodically cut it into five stacks of ten cards each, tossing the ace and king of clubs aside. His fingers knew the weight, shape and feel of each separate card with a memory of their own, just as they knew the sensation of Leslie's skin, the litheness and firmness of her body, the delicate musculature of the underside of her arms as she lifted them to encircle his neck, the curve of her breast, the smooth planes of her hips. With the surge of memory his throat went dry. God, he wanted her. And he was a fool.

He reached for the glass of orange juice, with his other hand turning up the cards one by one. Each one alternated: ace of spades, king of spades. Card tricks were the best part of magic, and the least used. An audience couldn't respond to such close digital manipulation; consequently the years it took to perfect such skills were wasted on performing magicians. Like most things, the rarer the skill the more valuable it became. And the more intriguing.

He had a brief vision of Leslie in shorts and sandals, her wheat-colored hair tousled mercilessly by the wind, laughing into the sun. He wanted intensely to see her like that, relaxed, at ease, unguarded. With him.

In sudden irritation he gathered the cards again and shuffled them one-handed, sipping his juice. Damn, he couldn't believe what he had said to her this afternoon. He couldn't believe how he had felt when he had said it. As though he meant every word.

It terrified him to realize that he still meant it. He did have every intention of falling in love with Leslie Roarke. He was half afraid he had done it already.

And it was crazy. She was right; they had no chance together. He was used to things coming easily to him and it was obvious nothing about Leslie would be easy. Everything about her was demanding, frustrating, impossible. But when she smiled, the way she had this afternoon over that silly rose, his heart actually stopped beating. And when she looked at him with those half-cautious, half-hopeful eyes, completely unaware that she was looking that way at all, he wanted to enfold her in his arms and hold her, just hold her until time itself was no more than a memory.

If he had any sense at all, he would stay as far away from her as possible. Michael had spent a lifetime avoiding constrictive relationships, and of all the women in the world, she was not the one for him.

Except that she was the only woman in the world for him. She didn't trust him. He wasn't sure she liked him. This afternoon when she'd stood between him and a door that wouldn't open she'd reminded him of a trapped rabbit, and it had broken his heart. She had looked, at that moment, exactly as he felt now, aching for her and knowing that there were more than doors to be broken down before he could have her...or escape from her.

A whole summer. Damn, how was he supposed to stay away from her the whole summer?

He swore loudly and viciously as a miscalculation sent the cards in his hand flying all over the boat's deck. A perfect example of what she was doing to him already, and he'd known her for less than a week. That had never happened to him before, not ever. He was a fool for letting it get started now.

Angrily, he tossed down the one remaining card in his hand, and it gazed back up at him benignly in the dying sun. The queen of hearts.

He smiled, slowly, ruefully and leaned back in his chair. He thought that what was really foolish was spending the weekend alone when she was so near, so lovely, and so very much wanted.

After all, why fight fate?

LESLIE WAS JUST HELPING an excited, incoherently chattering Tony out of her car the next morning when a sparkling white Rabbit convertible swung into the space next to hers and Michael Bradshaw grinned and lifted his hand in greeting. His timing was, as usual, impeccable.

He got gracefully out of the car and came around to her, sunlight washing over his white shorts and bright red polo shirt, glistening on the pale hairs of his bare legs and arms. He looked today just as she had always imagined him looking when he was at his leisure, and for a moment the real-life picture was so much like the imagined one that she felt disoriented, a little dazed.

It was, therefore, Michael who spoke first, direct and to the point. "I thought you might like to spend the day at the beach."

His eyes were covered by dark sunglasses, but his grin was contagious, and Leslie found herself returning it before she even knew what she was doing. "Thanks," she replied, shouting a little to make herself heard over the very vociferous Tony, "but my day is already filled." She gestured. "This is Tony Swan, one of my patients."

Michael removed his glasses, letting them dangle from the cord around his neck. The moment he did, silence fell, and Tony stood there, staring up at him soberly. "Hello, Tony." He smiled at the boy and extended his hand. After only a moment's hesitation, Tony imitated the gesture, allowing Michael to shake his hand. Leslie had never seen him do anything like that before. "I'm Michael, and right off hand I'd say you're the perfect stroke of luck—a built-in chaperone. What do you say you and I join forces to persuade this lady to take us to the beach?"

Leslie opened her mouth to explain that Tony couldn't understand all of what he said, much less answer him, but when Michael's smile moved from Tony to her there was no question in his eyes, and explanations seemed suddenly redundant. His hand was resting companionably on Tony's small shoulder and Tony, who, only a year ago, had been known to kick and bite like a badger whenever his personal space was invaded, did not seem to mind. He simply gazed up at Michael with those dark, mysterious eyes, twirling a lock of his hair around his finger in studious preoccupation, and waited.

Leslie said, "Did you really drive all the way out here on a Saturday without even considering that I might have other plans? It didn't occur to you to check with me first?"

His lazy smile sparkled sunshine in his eyes and made her forget, momentarily, the arrogance for which she had intended to upbraid him. "Why should I? As it happened, everything worked out fine."

"As it happens," Leslie explained to him, very patiently, "I *do* have other plans, as you can see. So, though I thank you for the offer—"

"Doesn't Tony like the water?" he interrupted, unperturbed.

Leslie hesitated, tempted. It was an extraordinary summer day, brilliant and calm, and how many times during the past week had she yearned to be on the Bay herself? Already her vacation tan was beginning to fade and she missed the gentle lull of the ocean, and she knew if she had not already committed her weekend elsewhere she would most likely have spent the day soaking up sun and watching the gulls. And it would serve Michael right if she said yes. A day with a screaming, obstreperous Tony might be just the dose of reality he needed.

She said, still reluctant, "Well, I *had* half considered taking Tony to the beach today. But crowds upset him and—"

"Then I've just solved your problem," Michael said confidently. "It just so happens I know a place where I can absolutely guarantee no crowds. Just the three of us."

Leslie thought about it, and the temptation was becoming harder and harder to refuse. Obviously, Tony liked Michael—anyone's guess why. And, oh, it would be lovely to spend the day with the sun and the water. If she passed up this chance, who knew when she might get another like it?

She looked at Michael for another moment, then nodded decisively. "All right," she said. "Thank you."

"I'll wait," he volunteered, "if you'd like to go inside and change."

"Into what?"

"Don't you want to bring a swimsuit?"

Leslie laughed. "I don't think either one of us is going to have much time for swimming this afternoon." Tony would be more than a handful for two reasonably competent adults, as Michael had yet to find out.

"What a shame," returned Michael with frank resignation. "I've been trying to picture you in a swimsuit all week. That's the main reason I planned this little outing, you know."

Leslie smirked at him. "Life is full of little disappointments, Mr. Bradshaw." She was wearing a long voile shirt over a short-sleeved stretch top and white cotton slacks, and though the outfit wouldn't be inappropriate for the beach, it did occur to her to change into something cooler in anticipation of the heat of the day. But a streak of irrational stubbornness seized her and she suddenly did not want to give Michael the satisfaction. Her father was always complaining about the way she dressed, too.

She glanced back toward the house. "Should we pack a lunch?"

"All taken care of," he assured her, and closed his hand around hers with a little tug. "Now, if you can't think of any more excuses..." He cocked his head toward her mockingly.

Leslie looked at him for a moment, then at Tony, whose solemn temperament couldn't possibly be expected to last much longer. *All right, Mr. Michael Bradshaw. You asked for this one.* She lifted her shoulders acquiescently. "I'm ready."

Tony was safely buckled into the back seat, still without uttering so much as a peep, the wind was whipping through her hair and the tailored landscaped of her residential neighborhood was rushing past them before Michael suggested, "Tell me about Tony."

"His official diagnosis is infantile autism," Leslie replied, digging through her purse for her sunglasses. "That's a catch-all term that encompasses a whole variety of symptomology. Basically, he has an immeasurable IQ with streaks of geniuslike behavior, a total inability to communicate on any level and a distorted perception of spatial relationships. He literally lives in another world, and doesn't recognize reality as we know it."

Michael slid a perceptive glance her way. "Which may not be such a bad thing," he murmured. "Does he understand what's being said to him?"

Leslie found her sunglasses and slipped them on. "Selectively. Like most kids, he hears and understands only what he wants to. You can sit right in front of his face and talk to him until you're hoarse and he won't bat an eyelash to let you know he hears you. But peel a candy wrapper across the room and behind his back and you've got his instant attention. At first they thought his speech problem was because of hearing loss, but he obviously hears as well as you or I—and I wouldn't wonder if he understood a lot more than most people, in his own way."

And then, because she was beginning to feel a small stirring of guilt, she felt compelled to point out, "He doesn't react to new situations very well, I'm afraid. I hope you have strong nerves; he's very easily overstimulated."

Michael glanced into the rearview mirror, where his tawny eyes met a soft, sober pair of dark ones. He winked at Tony and replied, "He seems calm enough now."

Leslie glanced back where Tony sat, sedate and observing, in the back seat. He had even stopped twirling his hair. "He's having one of his calm spells." She shrugged. "It won't last long."

But, taking advantage of his benign temperament while it lasted, Leslie twisted in her own seat and began to play a finger game with Tony. Usually Tony was most responsive to this sort of educational game—anything involving digital manipulation fascinated him—but today he wasn't interested. His attention seemed to be totally absorbed by the stranger who had invaded their midst.

By the time Michael pulled into the marina, Leslie was half ready to accuse him of putting the boy under a spell, for Tony usually reacted badly to car trips and he had never been silent for so long around a stranger before. He seemed completely fascinated by Michael—the sound of his voice, the movement of his head, the occasional glimpse of his eyes he caught in the rearview mirror. All of which were very positive signs—being able to respond to people outside the familiar faces of his family and therapists was an important part of his overall progress—but Leslie couldn't help being a little puzzled.

When they got out of the car Tony unfastened his seat belt and clambered out without any prompting, completely ignoring the bright, busy pier for the more fascinating absorption with Michael's face. "Are you going to rent a boat?" Leslie asked, thinking how perfect that would be and at the same time wondering how long she could count on Tony to sit quietly and stay out of trouble on a small outboard surrounded by water.

"Nope," replied Michael as he went down on his haunches before Tony. "What d'you say, tiger, you think you're big enough to crew my ship? I could use a strong first mate."

"Michael," said Leslie, delighted, "you have your own boat?"

Michael grinned up at her. "More or less. It'll serve our purpose for today, anyway. The engine overheats if you try to go more than four knots, but it should get us to a private cove I know about and back just fine." He looked back at Tony. "Ready to be piped aboard?"

Tony reached out soberly and removed Michael's sunglasses.

Leslie laughed out loud in the sudden pleasure of revelation. "That's it!" she exclaimed. "Your eyes!"

Michael gave her a puzzled glance, and then made a slight grimace of understanding. "Oh, yes. Awful, aren't they?"

"Awful?" Leslie's voice rose in incredulity while

Tony's eyes never wavered from Michael's. "Incredible, is what they are. Don't you like them?"

"I hate them. You're the only woman I've ever met whose first words to me weren't 'what happened to your eyes?'"

Leslie laughed, finding this confession both enlightening and endearing. What she had always considered his most remarkable physical characteristic was the one he was most ashamed of, and that only reminded her how very little she really knew about Michael and how much she wished to know. "Well," she said, "Tony seems to think your eyes are pretty wonderful...and actually, if you want to know the truth, I've never thought they were all that bad myself."

For a moment those strange, sun-warmed yellow eyes met hers in a gaze so soft and smiling and so redolent with things unsaid that Leslie felt her heart speed in response. But then, before the moment could grow uncomfortable, Michael turned back to Tony, lifting the small boy onto his hip. "All right, landlubbers, let's weigh anchor and get this tub under way. All aboard!"

Chapter Eight

Leslie followed Michael a short way down the pier to the cabin cruiser whose freshly painted blue hull announced in white letters that they were preparing to board the *Annabelle Lee*. Leslie cast him a sly look beneath her glasses. "Old girl friend?"

"Old poem," he corrected. "I've always had a weakness for Poe."

Leslie murmured, "You would have." He flashed a grin at her.

Leslie was a bit worried about how Tony would react to crossing the small ramp that spanned the water from dock to deck, but he was entirely too busy studying Michael's strangely colored eyes at close distance to even notice. Michael sprang lightly onto the deck and, setting Tony on his feet, extended his hand to help Leslie.

She had never seen him look quite so vibrant, so relaxed, content and at home. He always radiated a level of energy that was as much a part of his fascination as was his grace of movement and his quick, brilliant smiles, but today the sunlight seemed to form a golden aura about him, warming and embracing anything that came within his reach.

Leslie felt the power of that embrace as their hands briefly clasped, and a reluctance to break the contact that surprised her. The wind ruffled his hair and drew her attention to those narrow squint lines around the smooth tan skin of his eyes, which deepened a fraction with his smile as though he, too, felt the need to hold on to her a moment longer...as though, with his smile, he promised that there would be a time when both of their wishes would be fulfilled.

But he only suggested, "Why don't you two go explore below deck while I get us under way? I'm not so sure it would be a good thing for Tony the Tiger here to be on deck once the water starts moving."

Leslie, surprised at his perception, agreed completely and reached for Tony's hand as Michael showed them the way below. Though demonstrating an obvious reluctance to leave Michael, Tony did not voice any protests as they descended the narrow ladder into the living quarters.

Leslie was not certain just what she had expected. She supposed she had somehow assumed this was just a recreational cruiser, leased for the summer and outfitted for short overnight trips, the indulgence of a pleasure-oriented single male with nothing else to spend his money on. What she found was a cozy little apartment with all the conveniences of home.

Tony immediately found the television set and plopped down in front of it, not in the least disturbed when the reception began to go as they got under way. While he sang along wordlessly and at the top of his lungs with commercial jingles he knew by heart, Leslie explored her surroundings with growing interest.

It was a single room divided by counters and furniture arrangements into separate living, sleeping and cooking areas. The small bathroom—a utilitarian affair with sink, toilet and shower, no bathtub—was a separate enclosure at the foot of the ladder that led to the deck. Near the queen-size bed was a closet with space-saving sliding doors and a compact bureau that also served as a nighttable. Bookshelves flanked the bed and lined the space between the two portholes, and she had to kneel on the bed to read the titles. Sprinkled in among paperback mysteries and popular best-sellers were less common tomes, some of them college textbooks and reference works on American literature, by far the preponderance of them concerning matters of the occult, of ritual, mysticism and magic: *The Golden Bough*, *Witchcraft in Colonial America*, *Ancient Tribal Rites of Magic*, *Secrets of the Shaman*, *The Life of Houdini*, *The Last Illusion*.

Leslie found it vaguely disturbing to discover such overwhelming evidence of a preoccupation with the supernatural, until she reminded herself of his profession. How much time must he have spent immersing himself in the very essence of magic to be as good as he was? A lifetime, obviously.

She remembered how he had manipulated her letter opener, just a little something he did to occupy his hands, without thinking about it, without almost even being aware of it. It would have to become second nature to him, an autonomic impulse like drawing a breath or allowing the heart to beat.

She wondered what kind of man it took to devote himself so completely to the pursuit of such skills, and she could come up with only one answer: the kind of man she would never understand. And that was maddening.

A comfortable sitting area was composed of a deep, cushioned love seat, an easy chair, and a narrow cocktail table. The floor lamps, which added such warmth and livability to the room, were bolted to the floor. In addition to the color television set, Michael also had a VCR and a compact stereo with an impressive collection of audio and video tapes. His tastes in video entertainment leaned heavily toward fantasy-adventure; his tastes in music ranged from Mozart to Willie Nelson, from Abba to Frank Zappa, and just about everything in between. Leslie marveled over his ingenuity in simply creating a space for everything.

But by far the most fascinating aspect of his apartment was his kitchen—Leslie supposed it was technically a galley, but there was none of the sparse utilitarian atmosphere usually associated with the term ''galley'' in reference to food preparation here. Leslie had spent years planning her dream kitchen, and what she had finally come up with paled in comparison with this efficient, high-tech, ultra-sophisticated gourmet fantasy.

Not a single inch of space was wasted. Saucepans, crepe pans and light skillets hung from overhead hooks, and on the beams from which they were suspended were specially designed shelves where fresh herbs dried on flat glass plates or were stored in colorful jars. On the wraparound counters terraced elevations provided a separate space for an earthenware electric dutch oven, a pasta maker—Leslie's eyes lit up with envy when she saw that—and an elaborate food processor that combined blender, dough mixer, meat grinder, and juicer all in one. A microwave, browning unit and drying rack were built into the wall. His cabinets were equipped with rotation shelves, well-stocked with basic ingredients essential to any proud cook, and a number of rare imported delicacies made Leslie's mouth water when she saw them.

She had thoroughly explored his refrigerator and was once again perusing the titles of his books when she noticed the innocuous-looking chest at the foot of his bed. Leslie knew instantly that that was where he kept his magic props. Feeling like an overly curious Pandora, she knelt beside it to lift the lid. It was, of course, locked.

She found that unbearably frustrating. She knew what would be in it. Collapsible wands, interchangeable metal rings, false thumbs, scarves, paper flowers... Well, all right, she admitted grudgingly, perhaps items a bit more sophisticated than those, but props nonetheless. Just the very ordinary and quite explicable fare of a magician's trade, the key that would unlock his secrets and strip them of their drama. She knew what the chest contained, but still she wanted to see for herself, to touch the mundanities behind his mystery as though by doing so she could make him a little less incredible and a bit more real, more understandable.

She heard the engines stop and she gave the locked trunk

a grimace and a slight, rather childish, nudge with her toe, then went to pry Tony away from the television set so they could return to the deck. Tony resisted, as he always did when television time was over, shouting at her and lunging for the now blank television screen. Leslie fended him off routinely, for she had by now learned the easiest methods by which to avoid his sharp teeth and nails, gouging elbows and sneakered feet. She kept her voice low and firm, her grip insistent but not severe, for she knew that releasing his frustration in this way was one of the few outlets Tony had, and certainly he needed every escape valve he could get.

She didn't know how long Michael had been standing there watching them before he strolled in casually, announced, "How about a little fresh air and sunshine, Tiger?" and scooped Tony effortlessly out of Leslie's combative arms. After a few more purely leftover flails Tony settled down immediately, propped his hand on Michael's shoulder, and looked at Leslie with guileless sobriety.

Leslie, pushing back a few strands of hair from her damp face, cast Michael a dryly admiring look. "The magic touch, hmm?" she murmured.

"Must be," he replied easily, and ran an affectionate hand though Tony's hair. "Most people," he pointed out meaningfully to Leslie, "like me on sight."

"Most people," she replied just as pointedly, a spark of amusement dancing in her eyes, "are very easily taken in."

"Or maybe it has something to do with touching after all," he returned, still resting the light-framed boy against his hip. "Not a bad therapy. You should try it sometime."

"Thank you, I'm fully aware of the beneficial effects of touch therapy." *Especially yours*, she added silently and his eyes seemed to read the unspoken words and respond to them as swiftly and as warmly as though they had actually touched.

Because the simple memory of the last time she had been in his arms was enough to make her blood thrum, she felt a change of subject was in order. She gestured to their surroundings with a light of real wonder and interest in her eyes as she said, "Michael, do you actually live here?"

"Uh-huh." He set Tony on the floor and crossed over to the galley area, opening the refrigerator. "For the summer, anyway, though I'd like to make it more permanent." He cast her a glance that was peculiarly shy as he removed a pitcher of juice and confessed with a grin, "My secret ambition has always been to sail around the world. I doubt if I'll make it in this old tub, but it's a start, anyway. Would you like some wine?"

"Sure." Leslie felt a secret thrill as she remembered how she had always imagined him on the deck of a ship, and seeing him now, hearing him share a secret fantasy that was so much like the one she had invented for him, was such a wonderful blend of daydream and reality that she hardly knew how to react to it.

Michael poured two tumblers of juice and returned the pitcher to the refrigerator as he withdrew a bottle of white wine. Leslie inquired, "So why don't you? Sail around the world, I mean."

He laughed softly, reaching overhead for one of the wineglasses that hung from a suspended rack on the ceiling. "Darling, I'm not a millionaire. Outfitting this rig just about took care of what economists would refer to as my 'disposable income,' and more."

Leslie liked the way he said that, without artifice or presumption: *Darling.* As easily as though he had been calling her that all his life. She teased. "What? The great magician can't conjure up a few hundred thousand dollar bills? I'm disappointed!"

He turned, assuming thoughtfulness as he handed her the glass of wine. "Actually," he admitted, "I probably could. But I think it's illegal. And not quite—" he underscored the following word with his smiling eyes "—ethical."

Leslie lifted an eyebrow. "There's a code of ethics in your profession?"

"There's a code of ethics in my *life*," he responded, and

his eyes had lost their teasing as he tilted his head a bit and lifted his glass of juice to her in a small salute.

Leslie didn't know how to respond to that, and he saved her the awkwardness by picking up Tony's glass of juice and turning to the young man with an enthusiastic jerk of his head. "Come on, Tiger, I saw a whole school of fish swimming off the bow when we pulled in. They looked like shad, but they could have been dolphins for all I know. Let's go check it out."

Leslie followed them smiling, having not a doubt in the world that Michael could turn shad into dolphins if he so desired.

He had pulled into a beautiful sandy cove inaccessible by any means other than boat, and they had the place all to themselves. Tony, excited by the brilliance of the sun-sparked aqua water surrounding them, ran from rail to rail, chattering at the top of his lungs. Michael spoke to him in a calm, friendly tone, pointing out the occasional fish and identifying wild plants on the shore, explaining what made the water so bright here and so dark there, completely undistracted by the fact that Tony did not comprehend a word he was saying and most of the time was shouting so rapidly and so loudly that the sound of Michael's voice was completely drowned out.

Leslie was amazed, though why she should be she didn't know. That Michael was a man of great patience was a given; the level of tolerance and concentration it would take to deal with a boy like Tony would come naturally to him. She simply never would have guessed that he would be the type of man to give up his Saturday to entertain a difficult, emotionally and mentally handicapped child—and Michael seemed to be enjoying every moment of it.

When Michael wandered over to a table and began to absently shuffle a deck of cards, Tony ceased his chattering and followed him as though some invisible wire connected them. "Aha," Michael said, smiling at him, "so you want to see a little magic?"

Leslie, amused, drew closer as Michael's long, lithe fingers began to work the cards with a rapidity that was stunning. How she did love to see his hands move. She had never considered before the power a man's hands could have over a woman's erogenous zones, but she thought Michael's hands were without a doubt one of the sexiest things about him.

Michael began his careless patter as he worked the cards, never once taking his eyes off Tony's. "All right, Tiger, you are about to see one of the most incredible feats of prestidigitation ever known to man, last performed at the court of Queen Elizabeth the Second and before that handed down for generations among a select few members of a highly secret society known as the Keepers of the Sword. Kindly keep your eyes on the cards and you will notice that each and every member of the deck is present and accounted for—" He fanned the cards, closed them, shuffled them again. "I learned the secret from a beautiful gypsy girl who parted with it only after...well, I think we won't go into that, not until you're a little older, anyway. Now, behold and observe." He fanned the cards again, and every one of them was the ace of spades.

Tony, regarding the cards with nothing short of apathy, made no sound, and Michael glanced up at Leslie with a resigned quirk of the eyebrow. "Perhaps a bit too sophisticated, hmm?"

"Perhaps," Leslie agreed, although she personally would have loved to see the trick again. She hadn't once seen him make the switch.

Tony gathered up the cards with movements somewhat more clumsy than Michael's, and began to chant exuberantly to himself. Leslie worried that Michael might object to Tony's damaging his cards, but Michael watched him with tolerant amusement—and then growing amazement— as Tony shuffled the deck soberly, cut it, spread the cards to show a normal playing deck, shuffled again, and spread fifty-two aces of spades across the table.

For a moment Michael was utterly silent, staring at the little boy, then at the cards, then at Tony again. Then he murmured, "So, a wise guy, huh?" And Leslie burst into uncontrollable laughter.

"I should have warned you," she managed after a moment. "He's very imitative!"

Michael shared with her a slow, wonderful grin that seemed as much in delight over her laughter as in appreciation of the moment, then he got to his feet, lifting Tony to the seat he had just vacated. "Well, young fellow, looks like you've found something to keep you entertained for a while. Let me know when you're ready to apply for your union card."

"He'll stay with it for hours," Leslie said, watching Tony settle down to repeat his newly learned trick, over and over again. "He has absolutely no conception of time."

She glanced up at Michael as he took up his glass and, touching her back lightly, led her over to the rail, away from the noise of Tony's preoccupied chatter. "You're very good with him," she said sincerely. "It was nice of you to give up your Saturday this way."

"I like him," Michael replied simply, and leaned back against the rail, sipping his juice as he watched Tony. "And what makes you think I've given up anything?"

"Somehow," replied Leslie wryly, "I don't think this is what you had in mind when you planned a day of sea and sun with me."

He looked offended. "My dear Dr. Roarke, you give me absolutely no credit for depth. I don't *always* think with my hormones, you know."

Leslie felt no shame for her cutting remark of the previous day. She sipped her wine complacently. "Oh, no? And what, then, did you have in mind when you came to my house this morning?"

He replied easily, still watching Tony, "Wild sex and uninhibited passion, of course." And then he looked at her, his eyes as guarded and as unreadable as though the dark glasses that now hung around his neck were still hiding them. "What makes you think I didn't get exactly what I expected—your companionship?"

Leslie asked curiously, "Why?"

He chuckled then sipped his drink again. "I do believe you ask that question more than any woman I've ever known. That, and 'how?'"

Leslie shrugged. "It's my job."

"Knowing all the answers takes all the adventure out of life, Dr. Roarke."

"I'm not looking for adventure. I'm looking for the truth."

The exchange was quiet, casual and fraught with unstated meaning that was reflected in each gaze as they met each other's eyes without uneasiness, without evasion and without challenge. In the moment they looked at each other a cautious exploration began, a tenuous touching, a measure of understanding that was given and received equally by both.

Michael said at last, "I'm not certain you even know, yet, what you're looking for." He smiled wryly. "Maybe when you find out, life will be easier for both of us. Meanwhile—" he drained his glass and pushed away from the railing "—I think I'll make the day a little easier for us all by fixing lunch."

"Do you need any help?" Leslie volunteered, tempted by the prospect of working in his kitchen.

"No, you stay and keep an eye on my friend there. It won't take long."

Leslie smiled at the way he said that, as though the responsibility for Tony had somehow shifted from herself to him, following a natural course of events she could not even begin to fathom. Sometimes, she had to admit grudgingly, Michael's innate sense of authority could be highly welcome.

Michael served a wonderful chilled lobster salad laced with the most delicate hint of a wine marinade Leslie had ever tasted. They ate on deck, Leslie trying every trick she knew to pry the secret of the marinade from Michael, while Tony methodically separated his salad into separate piles of coordinating colors and then became so entranced by the design that he refused to eat. An easy companionability developed between them over lunch, and by the time Michael discreetly removed Tony's salad platter and substituted a peanut butter-and-jelly sandwich, their eyes were meeting with friendly laughter and natural warmth that felt, for both of them, as though it had been there forever.

Michael insisted he needed no help with the dishes, and Leslie relaxed in a canvas lounge, sipping her second glass of wine while Tony returned purposefully to his cards. She was feeling spoiled and pampered and wonderfully luxurious. "We should take Tony into the water," Michael said when he returned. "Can he swim at all?"

"Not so soon after eating," Leslie returned drowsily, and then had to smile, realizing how domestic they sounded—he the enthusiastic father and she the protective mother.

Michael sank into the chair beside her, his tautly muscled thighs comfortably spread apart, his hands folded on his spare torso. He hadn't put his sunglasses back on for Tony's sake, and his eyes, in the brilliance of the reflected sunlight, looked like mirrors. He was gazing absently over the peaceful, water-locked scene, and Leslie took advantage of the opportunity to study those eyes, which he found an embarrassment and she found so wonderfully intriguing. She could lose herself just looking at them. Remembering how dazed and alive they had looked yesterday after he had kissed her, how they sparked with mischief whenever she gave him opportunity to tease, how thoughtful or intimidating they turned at the most unexpected moments. And, as her imagination drifted on a haze of wine and warmth and sunshine, she could see those eyes dark and heavy and passion-sparked, gazing down into hers as they made love.

She said quickly, purposefully distracting herself, "We could use more help like yours at the hospital, you know. If you ever have any spare time you'd like to donate..."

His gaze returned to hers. "Careful. I might just take you up on that. I was under the impression you saw more of me than you wanted at the Center."

Leslie shrugged, a trifle uncomfortably, because she

knew that was exactly the impression she had intended to give, and it was a deliberately false one. "We both know what our professional differences are, Michael."

"But not our personal ones," he suggested softly, watching her.

Leslie couldn't remember, at that moment, what their personal differences were supposed to be, so she chose not to reply. Instead she turned her attention to Tony, who still sat at the card table in the shade, his tone rising and falling with dramatic nonsyllabic exclamations as he busily dealt out the cards. She smiled wistfully. "I'd give anything to know what he's saying."

"Or hearing," added Michael. "Or even seeing. What a fascinating world he must live in all by himself."

"But a lonely one," Leslie pointed out, and then their eyes met again, an unexpected shared exchange between two people who knew about loneliness. It was poignant, tender, and it touched Leslie in a way she couldn't understand.

"We all isolate ourselves in different ways, I suppose," Michael said simply, and then Leslie grew uncomfortable. She dropped her gaze.

Michael, after a moment, got up and went to join Tony at the card table, and Leslie closed her eyes against the sun, thinking about what he'd said. She had never thought of herself as lonely before. Certainly that was not a term she would have ever considered applying to Michael. But loneliness was one of those things that could very often go undetected until there was a standard by which to measure it. Until Michael Bradshaw had come into her life she had been content, busy and fulfilled. Before him, she had never known what she was missing, and now...

It didn't seem fair, somehow.

Lulled by the gentle rocking of the boat, the rhythmic slap of waves against the hull, the warm sun and excellent wine, Leslie closed her eyes. When she opened them again she thought she was dreaming.

Michael had resumed his seat across from her, lounging

back in his canvas chair, eyes obscured by dark glasses, and at first, in her half-dozing state, she thought he was completely naked. She closed her eyes again, soporific, and then curiosity overcame her and she had to open them. It was no dream.

Bare knees and lightly furred thighs were in her direct line of vision. Absorbing the rest of the landscape was a smooth expanse of golden naked chest and there—she released her breath cautiously—low on his waist, the band of his white shorts. He was pouring a measure of suntan oil into his palm and gently massaging it into his skin, his head tilted backward slightly to worship the sun, and he had never reminded her so strongly of a great jungle cat, lazily basking in the heat of the day.

Her eyes hidden by her own sunglasses, Leslie lay perfectly motionless, and, helpless to do anything else, watched him. His fingers slid over his strong, columnar throat, leaving a sheen of glistening oil that magnified the coarse masculine pores. She had always thought of Michael's skin as smooth and soft, but she could see the slight roughness now on his neck and his chin, generated by many mornings with a razor. His palm made lazy circular motions on his shoulder, fingers smoothing his biceps. When he stretched out one long forearm, brushing the oil along its length, Leslie could see the tendons that tautened to his muscled upper arm and the heavy tracery of blue veins beneath the olive skin. She watched his fingers move absently across those muscles and her own fingertips began to tingle as she imagined the strength and hardness beneath them.

He poured oil into the other hand and rubbed it into his opposite shoulder and arm, and Leslie, mesmerized, followed every movement.

His palm moved across his collarbone, fingers trailing briefly into the dip at his throat, and Leslie's pulse began to speed. His hand moved down, slowly and leisurely, across his chest. His skin glistened wherever his fingers touched. His palm made circles over first one breast muscle and then the other, his skin rippling slightly with the motion. His fingers absently brushed one flat brown nipple and then the other and Leslie's throat went dry, just watching him.

His hands glided downward over the skin of his torso, across his ribcage, and over his flat stomach, then upward again, and down, massaging the warm, slick oil into his flesh. Leslie's tongue felt swollen in her mouth, and she could feel her pulses thrumming. A stinging, languorous heat invaded her body that had nothing to do with the sun.

His chest, brown and glistening, was hairless until the point just above his navel, where a pale dusting of gold gathered and narrowed into his shorts. As Leslie watched, Michael smoothed oil onto that lower part of his abdomen, around his waist, lazy, sensuous motions. The sight of his oiled fingers absently tracing just a fraction inside his waistband made Leslie's throat convulse.

"Would you like to do my back?"

A startled leap of pulses sent heat rushing throughout her body and she wondered how long he had known she was awake, and whether he had staged the entire narcissistic display for her benefit. Anger, amusement and rueful embarrassment mixed with the lingering traces of arousal, and she thought that if she had learned nothing else today she had at least gained valuable insight into the female attraction to male exhibitionism. *Well done, Michael*, she thought, and hid a smile behind an exaggerated yawn and stretch as she replied drowsily, "No, thanks. You seem to be doing just fine by yourself."

Michael favored her with one of his slow half-grins, and capped the bottle of oil. "How about you?" he suggested. "Aren't you getting hot in all those clothes? I've got an old pair of swimming trunks you can wear."

Leslie chuckled throatily. "I'll just bet you do." And suddenly she sat up straight, looking around. "Where's Tony?"

"I thought he might be getting too much sun, so I took him below deck to watch television. When I left him he was sound asleep with a Superman movie blaring on the VCR. Poor little fellow was pretty well beat. He'll probably sleep for an hour or two.''

Leslie relaxed and sat back. Two things occurred to her then. The first was that she had been so absorbed by Michael when she first woke up that she hadn't even missed Tony until this minute. The second was that she felt so comfortable—so confident—with Michael that she had allowed herself to fall asleep, leaving the child for whom she was responsible in the hands of a man she barely knew. Was that a good thing, or bad?

Right at the moment, she felt very strongly that it was a good thing.

She slanted Michael a sleepy smile. ''Superman, huh? Let me guess—your hero. You always wanted to grow up to be Clark Kent.''

''Actually no,'' he replied quite seriously. ''I always wanted to grow up to be James Bond. Now *there's* a hero for you. He gets the bad guy, the secret formula *and* the girl, without fail, every single time.''

Leslie reached for her now-warm glass of wine from beneath the lounge. ''And with 007 as a role model you grew up to be a magician? How did that happen?''

''Easy. I found a way to do it all with half the trouble and none of the risks. Don't drink that warm, Les; it'll make you sick. Let me get you another glass.''

The half-empty glass of wine was whipped out of her hand before she could protest, and Michael disappeared behind the wheelhouse. That was the second time he had shortened her name. She found she rather liked it.

''Still sound asleep,'' he reported of Tony when he returned. The icy cold glass of wine was placed in her hand and Michael, with his tumbler of orange juice, sank into his chair again.

''You don't drink?'' commented Leslie.

''Only with meals. All of the ancient cultures considered wine a food, you know, and I think they had the right idea.''

"This is wonderful," murmured Leslie, sipping the wine. And then she cast him a sly glance. "Is *this* the secret ingredient in the marinade?"

He grinned. "I'll never tell."

"You're impossible." Her intended pout was spoiled by a long, sinuous stretch. Michael's eyes followed every motion of every muscle, and she could feel his gaze even through his sunglasses. It delighted her. "Locked trunks, secret recipes, occult illusions..."

He picked up on the first statement with a spark in his eyes. "Aha, so you've been trying to get into my treasure chest, hmm? Don't you know what happens to people who try to open boxes better left locked?"

Though she knew he was teasing, Leslie couldn't help feeling a little defensive. "Well, I didn't break it open or anything. I don't see why you keep it locked, anyway. There's nothing in there but stage props."

"Maybe," he suggested, "I locked it simply because I knew it would drive you crazy. Nothing is going to get your attention faster than something you can't get into, turn inside out and analyze to death. And I happen to enjoy being the one to drive you crazy."

Her look was filled with tolerance and laced with derision. "That's very infantile, Bradshaw."

He inclined his head modestly. "Thanks for the consultation, Dr. Roarke."

Leslie chuckled, sipping her wine. "You never did answer my question the other day," she said after a time, and she looked at him. "About why you quit performing."

Michael shifted his chair a little, turning it so that the full rays of the sun caught his gleaming chest, and his bare thigh was only inches from Leslie's elbow. "Television," he decided after a moment's thought.

She raised an eyebrow questioningly. "What?"

"Television, movies—hell, even the telephone," he explained. "Not to mention computers, space flight, satellite transmissions... Do you honestly understand how any of them work? But you accept them as part of your everyday life. There's no wonder to mysteries anymore, and illusions are so entwined with reality that all the challenge has gone out of making magic."

He shook his head slowly, a rueful half-grin touching his lips. "After a live show one night I heard a man explaining to his wife in all sincerity how my water illusion was just a camera trick—and she was believing every word of it. I'm sure they must have realized it later, but they were so immured to the media world that at that moment it didn't occur to either one of them that what they had seen was *live*. I knew right then that all the fun had gone out of performing."

"But you've worked so hard at it," Leslie insisted. "You must have, to be as good as you are. And you still keep in practice. Why, if you don't intend to ever perform again?"

He sipped his juice, his face in profile to her, and the soft curve of his lips was more reminiscent than amused. "I read a story one time, about a retired jewel thief. He spent the last ten years of his life planning to the last detail the greatest theft of the century, and when he finally carried it out no one ever knew what he had done—because he returned the merchandise before it was even missed. He didn't need the money, or the recognition or the risk of getting caught—he just needed to do it."

Michael lifted his lean, oiled shoulders in a graceful dismissal. "Magic, to a real magician, is not just a craft, skill or job; it's a part of your personality—of your soul, I guess And you keep doing it because, if you're good, the challenge doesn't stop when the applause does. Because, I suppose, you just have to keep doing it."

"So, basically," Leslie mused, groping for some insight into him, "the great illusionist got disillusioned."

"In a way, I suppose. Not with the art itself, but with the environment that surrounds it. The age of miracles is past, you know, sad but true. I've often thought I would have been happier if I had lived in the time of Merlin."

Leslie glanced at him slyly beneath her glasses. "Maybe you did."

He feigned amazement. "Why, Dr. Roarke, was that a profound statement I just heard coming out of your mouth? It'll never stand the scrutiny of the scientific method, you know."

Leslie smiled lazily. "I guess I've been hanging around you too long."

The expression on his face softened as he turned to her, and it was maddening to be unable to see his eyes. He lifted his glass slightly, and touched it to hers. "Then let's drink to the continuation of a very bad habit."

And that, Leslie realized with a sort of disturbed resignation, was exactly what he was threatening to become to her: a bad habit, dangerous to live with, impossible to live without. Subtly, from the very first day, he had begun to wedge himself into her life, and today had only made the secret invasion a more permanent one. She still understood him no better than she had before, knew him no better, but what she did know she liked—irrational as that was—and liked a lot. It was more than fascination. A curious warmth had begun to develop between them that seemed to have the potential to span their differences, and that was a frightening realization. Leslie didn't like to go into anything blind, and that was precisely how she felt with Michael— as though she were being led blindfolded down a darkened corridor with nothing but his hand to hold on to...and that hand could at any moment be jerked from her grasp.

In a curious kind of symbology, he reached for her hand then, almost as though he had sensed the doubts that had begun to pile up in the corners of her mind and wished to reassure her. His touch was warmed with the sun and again she recognized the sinewy strength of his fingers beneath the softness of his skin. He held her hand lightly, almost absently, turning it palm upward in the cradle of his own, and there was a tightening in Leslie's chest that felt like anticipation as she let him do, for the moment, what he would.

Michael said, thoughtfully, "That's interesting."

"What?"

"Your lifeline." A feather-light touch of his forefinger traced a line on Leslie's palm, making her skin tingle and urging her to close her hand around his touch. Then he turned his other hand palm upward and held it next to hers for her inspection. "Look. Your lifeline is almost a mirror image of mine."

All Leslie saw was how large and strong and competent his hand looked next to hers. She had never thought of him as a big man; physically he did not seem to dominate her and he was not more than a couple of inches taller than she, but seeing their hands together like that reminded her potently of the differences between men and women. It made her feel fragile and feminine, imagining her own vulnerability beneath the skillful caresses of his hands. And it was not a bad feeling.

She laughed a little nervously. "Michael, I don't know anything about lifelines. And you know perfectly well that the creases on a person's palm are simply physical traits, like hair or eye color."

"But look," he insisted, and she couldn't tell whether the note of curiosity in his voice was sincere or feigned. "If we put our hands together, like this—" he demonstrated, warmth seeping into her body from his at the light pressure "—our love lines intersect."

"Mmm." Leslie pretended interest, hoping that he would continue the gesture by entwining his fingers with hers, but, because she couldn't tell whether he was teasing, she was reluctant to do it herself. "Just as, I suppose, everyone else's love lines would if you put two hands together."

"No," he disagreed, quite seriously. "Actually, they wouldn't. The sizes of individual hands are too different for a perfect match, for one thing." He turned her palm over, once again cradling it in his hand, and studied it for another moment. He was silent for so long that Leslie began to wonder what he was seeing there.

"Well, swami?" she prompted.

He lifted his eyes to her, smiling faintly. His finger again began to trace the path of the lines on her hand, maddening, tantalizing little motions that she could feel all the way to the center of her abdomen. He said, "You have a very turbulent love line. The most important crisis of your emotional life is not very far away, but if you survive it, the love you've found will be strong enough to last a lifetime. It won't be easy," he said soberly, "but it will be worth it."

The sun-baked day seemed to radiate an inner heat within Leslie that was generated from the sensual, hypnotic brush of Michael's fingers against the highly sensitized nerves of Leslie's palm. The cooling sea breezes were brief and tantalizing caresses that promised, but did not deliver, the magic Michael's fingers could play on her skin. All her attention was focused on the slow, suggestive concentric circles he traced on her palm, becoming smaller and smaller, lighter and lighter, until her very flesh seemed ready to shriek for more of him.

Her throat felt heavy, and she had to clear it before she spoke. Still, she couldn't manage the light tone she had hoped for. What she managed, in fact, was little more than a whisper. "Don't you—Aren't you going to tell me whether...I will survive this supposed crisis?"

He smiled, and brought his head slowly down to her hand. He kissed her palm lightly. "I'm not omniscient, darling. There is always the element of human choice."

He laid her hand alongside his face, and instinctively, Leslie's fingers moved to caress the golden skin. A slight roughness outlined the shape of his beard, giving way to the smooth bridge of his nose, and the satiny softness of his lips. Leslie's breath caught as he parted his lips, and the tip of his tongue touched her nail. She let her finger slip inside another fraction and felt the slippery hard shape of his teeth, his tongue wetting the pad of her finger. And all the while his fingers were guarding the back of her hand, stroking it, caressing it, now moving her hand lightly over his face while his tongue traced a delicate, nerve-tingling pattern down the center of her palm.

The sensation was so subtly electrifying, so wonderfully promising, that Leslie had to close her eyes against it, releasing her breath in a slow stream of exquisite anticipation. She wanted then more than anything in the world to feel the caress of his lips, his tongue, on her throat, and her face, and her breasts. And even as her hand moved to close around the back of his neck and draw him closer she remembered the sleeping Tony; she pulled her hand away.

"We...have to be leaving soon," she said, with difficulty. "I promised Tony's mother he'd be back by five."

For a moment longer Michael held her hand lightly captured between his strong fingers, looking down at it with patent absorption. As always, he was impossible to read. Leslie ached to know what he was thinking, what he was feeling.

Looking back to her face, he said quietly, "We could drop him off...and then come back here." His lips toyed with an almost-teasing smile. "I'll let you play in my kitchen."

Leslie drew in her breath. Oh, yes, the moonlight glancing off the sea, a gourmet dinner by candlelight, and then... There was no element of guesswork in what would happen next. No choice.

"I'm not good with impulsive decisions, Michael. I always live to regret them."

For the first time she was glad that the dark glasses hid his eyes. She didn't think she wanted to know what he was thinking now. It was too easy to imagine.

The soft sound of his carefully released breath was the only outward betrayal of emotion. "I know," he said, and looked down again at her hand. "That's why I've promised myself to give you plenty of time to think it over." When he looked back up at her his smile was fleeting and strained. "Not very smart of me, huh?"

No, thought Leslie. *Not very smart at all.*

He took her hand and placed it very carefully on the arm of her chair, then he rose and went into the wheelhouse. A moment later she heard the engines start.

Chapter Nine

The five of them sat in the lab Michael had converted into his workspace and office, watching the latest videotape of the Gaynor twins. As the television screen reflected back the image of Kevin and Karen, their bodies taut, both pairs of eyes glazed with identical expressions, a one-pound weight on the table between them began to shudder and slowly levitate, hovering in midair for half a second before crashing down again. Michael pushed the pause button and crossed the room to where a similar worktable and the identical weight were set up for him. He stood before it for a moment, hands in pockets, concentrating. The weight began to shudder and lift, and then crashed to the table again.

He had demonstrated a similar illusion for every feat they had witnessed on videotape. Malcolm and George were getting restless; Winston had resorted to chewing on a pencil, his brow creased in an anxious scowl. Leslie's patience, never very great where Michael was concerned, was worn to its thinnest extension.

Malcolm said tightly, "I don't want you to think we don't appreciate your theatrics, Mr. Bradshaw—"

And George burst out, "For the love of Pete, man, do you think we didn't check that room for wires? We're not complete idiots, you know. Each one of these experiments was conducted under the strictest scientific supervision—"

Michael said calmly, turning to face them, "That particular illusion can be performed without levers or pulleys—without, in fact, any kind of equipment that your instruments would register."

Leslie said, with a cool lift of her eyebrow, "Then perhaps you would be good enough to explain to us just *how* it was done. So that we don't make the same mistake again."

In the week that had passed since she and Tony had spent the day with Michael on his boat, Leslie had seen very little of him. They passed in the corridor, and his smile was fleeting and absent. They said good morning and never stopped to chat. He was very busy, she knew. She was busy, too, spending more time at the hospital to make up for the previous time she had spent at the Center, and she told herself that the less she and Michael saw of each other the better. Chemistry was a dangerous thing, and if the two of them had been alone that day on the boat, without the distraction and the responsibility of Tony, she knew that her better judgment would not have prevailed over the insistence of her instincts. And she would be even now regretting that day.

She wondered if Michael had lost interest in her. Or if he, too, had come to see the wisdom of her decision.

Michael smiled at her. Still, when he smiled, even across a roomful of people, something strange happened inside her chest and all she wanted to do was smile back. "I can tell you how it *could* be done," he said. And then, glancing around at the other two scientists and Winston, he explained matter of factly, "An electronic remote control. Notice that Kevin kept his hands in his pockets the whole time. Any impulses that came from the device could easily be fed into your EEG monitoring equipment, so that it would register as nothing more than increased brain-wave activity—which, of course, is exactly what you expect to see. Or it would be picked up on a wide sweep as random electrical impulses, which wouldn't be unusual in a case like this, would it?"

Leslie swore, silently and viciously, over and over again.

Malcolm and George exchanged an uncomfortable look and shifted restlessly in their seats.

"So are you sure that's what these two are doing?" Winston demanded. "The whole thing is a setup, a con?"

"No," Michael replied mildly, "I'm not saying that at all."

"Well, damn it man," exploded Winston, "what *are* you saying?"

"What do you need for proof?" insisted Malcolm. "Do you want us to strip the kids naked and pop them in a hermetically-sealed room? Then will you be convinced they're not operating with remote controls or hidden tape recorders?" He turned angrily to Winston. "I was against this whole thing from the beginning, but I agreed to go along—and now look what it's gotten us. Nothing! A lot of possibilities and no firm decision one way or the other. Will you tell me again how this is supposed to help us?"

Resting his hip casually against the table and crossing his arms over his chest, Michael said, "I promised you no snap judgments. I also promised I wouldn't interfere with your work while I went about mine. Unless you want me to blow my cover—which would, I think, put a serious hole in your credibility with your case subjects—this is going to take time."

He paused to let his eyes roam over the group while the scientists digested this. "Now," he continued, "let's talk about possibilities. I've shown you all that these things can be duplicated—but I didn't say any of it was easy. We need to ascertain whether or not these kids are capable of creating these same effects by normal means." And his lazy, tawny eyes rested on Leslie. "Madame Resident Psychologist, that's where you come in. What kind of IQs are we dealing with here?"

Leslie hesitated. She felt like a traitor, and she thought briefly how much time and trouble could have been saved if she had only turned over the Gaynor file to Michael when he first asked. But, damn it, she still thought her decision had been the right one; just look at what was happening now. He was trying his best to twist the facts to his advantage, just as she had known he would.

But there was no point in evading any longer. She responded, "They're both fairly bright." A minor understatement! "Kevin a few IQ points higher than Karen." She met Michael's gaze evenly. "Kevin is also pretty much known as an electronics whiz."

She expected a flash of triumph, a smirk of I-told-you-so, and just like that, a shrug of his shoulders—file closed, case dismissed. What she got was a thoughtful nod, and silence.

Winston spoke up abruptly, "Look, Michael—all of you—" he swept a glance around the room "—I try not to interfere with your work. You pay me to keep things running smoothly so you don't have to worry about anything but doing what you do. But I think it's time to tell you we're getting some pressure on this thing. If we're not able to publish some results soon—"

"Publish!" exclaimed Leslie, sitting forward sharply. "We're not anywhere near ready to go public. Our own research has just barely gotten under way, and if Michael—" She did not finish the sentence. If Michael hadn't raised doubts, if he was right, if he had never appeared on the scene, things would be much easier now, much clearer.

Winston spread his hands in a frank gesture of resignation. "Look, I don't know what to tell you. We've got a lot riding on these two kids—more than just the time and money we've invested in the research. They can make us or break us; you all know that. If they're on the level—and we have no concrete proof that they're not—" he cast a quick look at Michael "—then we need to go with them, go with them fast, and in a big way. But if they're not, we need to get rid of them quick, and allocate our funds elsewhere. That's the long and short of it, boys and girls. We've got to take a position."

Leslie took a breath. She looked at her two colleagues, and their faces reflected the same indecision that was in her own. They were confident in their research methods, experienced enough to rely on their own data...but cautious about making a judgment.

If Michael Bradshaw hadn't strolled in here and proceeded to make them painfully aware of how easily they could be fooled, if he hadn't injected such a patent note of cynicism into the proceedings, there would be none of the uncertainty that was afflicting them now. They would have, perhaps, even been persuaded to publish a cautious, conservative, fact-filled report on what they had discovered so far, thereby placating Winston and buying time. But Michael had come, he had made them doubt, and now no one was willing to commit to anything. Least of all Leslie.

Malcolm said, "This could be a media circus, Winston. Our careers are on the line."

"More than that," countered Leslie, "the entire future of psychic research."

Michael addressed Winston. "I strongly advise against any publicity right now. If you're right, you're right. But if you're wrong...it could be the biggest mistake you ever made in your lives. I think it's worth a little time, don't you, to avoid a disaster like that?"

There was a hesitation, a moment of shared discomfort, and Leslie had to fight down the irrational anger she could feel building toward Michael. He was right. That was what she hated the most. Everything she had ever known about herself—the precision, the conservatism, the dedication and the pedantic attention for detail—shouted at her that he was right. But a part of her, just as strong and just as determined, maintained a firm and defensive position for the Gaynors.

Perhaps Kevin was smart enough to have rigged everything electronically; there was no evidence that that was what he *had* done. Even Michael admitted that. The twins were also insecure, defensive and basically unstable personality types, and shared perhaps a half dozen other psychological problems she would have liked to investigate more thoroughly—but none of that had any bearing whatsoever on whether or not they possessed psychic ability.

Leslie, like Malcolm and George, had been in this sort of research too many years not to recognize genuine evidence of psi phenomena when she saw it. And like Malcolm and George, she was forced to allow Michael a chance to prove her wrong.

It didn't occur to her that she was for the first time in her professional career taking an assertive stand based on nothing but subjective judgment. And that she was doing so for no other reason than to prove Michael wrong.

George spoke abruptly into the silence. "Before we go any further I think we should all take a look at this." He got to his feet and withdrew from his lab-coat pocket another videotape. "I just made this this morning. I think you'll all find it rather...surprising."

He removed the old tape from the machine, inserted the new one, and engaged the playback mechanism. Without further prelude, they watched the figures flash into prominence on the screen.

"Apparently they've been working on this for some time," George said. "According to Kevin, they've had the ability for years, but the problem was controlling it. They wanted to show me before they showed anyone else."

Kevin and Karen sat in the same laboratory, on opposite sides of the metal table. Between them was a two foot section of a four-by-four wooden stud, upon which they focused their concentration. Their hands were linked on top of the table.

From the center of the block of wood a small tendril of smoke began to curl. It thickened and spread, and a small circle of wood at its source began to glow red. Karen coughed, narrowing her eyes against the escalating onslaught of smoke. And suddenly the entire four-inch-thick block burst into flames, causing the boy and girl to jump back abruptly, toppling over their chairs in their haste. An attendant rushed into the frame, grabbing a fire extinguisher from the wall, and the tape ran out.

The silence in the room was thick enough to cut. Winston was poised excitedly on the edge of his seat; Malcolm looked stunned. Leslie *felt* stunned. Michael's expression was at its most exasperatingly enigmatic.

Malcolm broke the silence by muttering something very earthy, but oddly appropriate, giving George his cue to elaborate. "The wood came from my office, where the workmen are repairing a set of shelves. I picked it at random and checked it thoroughly, there was no chance that it could have been treated beforehand. And the kids took no matches or ignition devices of any kind into the room with them. Same laboratory setup, all equipment functioning normally."

Leslie murmured, "It must have taken a tremendous amount of heat for it to burst into flames the way it did—so quickly."

Winston said, shaking his head slowly, "I've never seen anything like it, and I thought I'd seen everything. Good Lord, do you realize what this could mean?"

"What the hell were they keeping it such a big secret for?" Malcolm demanded.

Michael said easily, "I want to examine the evidence, of course. And talk to the kids. Do you think they'd be willing to try this again?"

George met his eyes with challenge in his own. "I don't know why not. They've always been *very* cooperative."

Michael only smiled. "So they have."

The organization of the meeting broke down completely after that. This unexpected development called for a complete redefinition of priorities. A concentrated schedule of controlled experiments was drawn up, and Michael insisted upon being present at each one. Leslie marked off extra appointment time for consultation with the twins. Something about their use of fire, given what she knew about their background, bothered her immensely. But she had not analyzed it clearly enough in her own mind to draw a conclusion. And Winston, with avarice in his eyes, urged them to hurry, not to waste a moment. This could really be it. The breakthrough for which they had waited for years.

Leslie found that, by some trick of circumstances, she

was the last to leave when they all filed out. Michael stood at the door, and they were momentarily alone. He said, "Are you going to the hospital this afternoon?"

"As a matter of fact, I am. I probably should stay here and try to talk to the twins today, but I have other appointments I can't break."

"I'd like to come along with you," he volunteered, and withdrew a small white box from his pocket. "I have a present for Tony. I would have given it to you earlier, but I haven't seen you much this week." His look was not accusing, but it easily suggested the fact that she had been avoiding him. Leslie wondered briefly and guiltily if that was true, when all the time she had been busily trying to convince herself it was the other way around.

"It's a deck of cards," he explained, tucking the box back into his pocket. "I thought if he's going to be a pro, he might as well practice on his own deck."

When she still hesitated, he cocked his head slightly and reminded her, "You invited me to drop in anytime."

"Oh…oh, yes of course." She wondered how he had known she was going to be seeing Tony today. And she also wondered what made her heart feel so light in her chest at the possibility of spending another afternoon with him. She tried to keep her voice noncommittal. "I mean…Tony will be delighted, I know, and it was sweet of you to think of him, but I can't let you sit in on any of my sessions."

"I'll stay completely out of your way," he promised gravely, and placed his hand lightly upon her back to escort her out.

"Shouldn't you be staying here, though—working on a new illusion to discredit the Gaynors?"

Leslie was surprised by the bitterness that was reflected in her tone, for after a week of hardly seeing him at all, she did not want to spoil their afternoon together by starting an argument with him. But Michael only laughed. "How many times do I have to tell you that's what I'm *here* for. It's my job."

"But for heaven's sake, Michael, so far you haven't told

us a single thing." Her tone was irritable, but she did not
shrug away from the light touch of his hand on her back.
"All you've done is cause a lot of confusion and slow
down our work. Don't you have any opinion at all?"

Their footsteps echoed dully on the pine-floored foyer as
they entered the main lobby. Michael was thoughtful for a
moment. "Actually, I do have an opinion. I just didn't think
you'd be interested in it."

She cast him an exasperated look. "Now why in the
world would you think that?"

"You haven't noticed?" The lift of his eyebrow was
mild and nonaccusatory. "You've already formed your
own opinion—quite unlike the methodical, facts-only scientist I always took you to be—which accepts without
question everything the Gaynors claim to be. And at this
very tenuous stage in our relationship, I'm not all that anxious to disillusion you."

"Don't be ridiculous," Leslie snapped. She didn't know
whether she was more disturbed by his suggestion of nar-
row-mindedness on her part, or by his reference to their so-
called relationship, which, besides the fact that it didn't
exist, had nothing whatsoever to do with anything. Or at
least it shouldn't have. "You know we haven't compiled
enough evidence to form an opinion one way or another—
and you're certainly not helping matters any."

"All right." They stepped out into a day that was heavy
and overcast, threatening late-afternoon thundershowers.
Without his being aware of it, Michael's hand drifted down
to Leslie's waist, a lightly protective, gently caressing gesture. "I think that Kevin and Karen Gaynor are two slightly
disturbed, very insecure young people who are so impatient
for recognition—of any kind—that they'd do anything to
get it. They may even have some mild telepathic ability,
but there's something about them that just won't let me
believe they can do everything they claim to. I think it's
more than possible that they're enhancing whatever psychic
ability they have with deliberate technological tricks."

Leslie drew in her breath softly. She could not refuse to

recognize that Michael's description of the twins sounded very much like her own privately formed clinical judgment, but his cynicism seemed to be clouding the issue, not clearing it. She said coolly, ''It's been my experience that when you look for problems, problems are exactly what you find. What you've got to realize, Michael, is that fraud has been the exception and not the rule in our kind of research. Very often we've found that people come to us with phenomena that can be explained by normal means, but they're as surprised as anyone else when we're able to show them that what they've experienced is not inexplicable, just unfamiliar. Rarely—very rarely—do we ever come upon anyone who's deliberately trying to trick us. And I fail to see what makes you so certain that the Gaynors fall into this small category...conveniently, just in time for you to expose them.'' She lifted her shoulders lightly, feeling the brush of Michael's fingers on her ribcage as she did so. ''If it's true, then prove it. If you can't, it seems to me we have no choice but to accept the more likely possibility, and investigate the case as genuine evidence of psi.''

Michael should have been offended, or annoyed at the very least, by her implications and her casual dismissal of his intent. Instead he discovered quite unexpectedly how much he liked the clipped, remote tone of her voice, the imperious lift of her head, the way she straightened her shoulders in instinctive preparation for combat. He liked her soft and dewy-eyed, he liked her laughing and teasing, and he liked it when the blood rushed to her cheeks with embarrassment or surprise. And he liked her angry, authoritative and determined.

God, how he'd missed her this past week. He'd been determined to play by her rules, giving her time and space, doing nothing that could be remotely construed as pressure or persuasion...hoping, perhaps, that she would come to miss him, too. Perhaps he should have kept to the plan and waited for her to come to him. For now, feeling the delicate warmth of her skin through the material of her blouse, watching the way a gust of wind flicked a strand of that funny-colored hair over her shoulder and caused her to reach up an impatient hand to brush it back, he felt a surge of longing so intense that it was almost painful.

But Michael was accustomed to disguising his emotions, and with a nod of his head and a slightly guiding pressure on her back, he said, "We'll take my car." Then, "As for the Gaynors, their preoccupation with fire may be their undoing. If they're doing what I think they are, we should be able to wrap this case up in a matter of days."

Leslie glanced at him, but knew it was useless to ask him to elaborate. She found herself hoping, intensely, that whatever it was Michael was thinking, he was wrong.

TONY WAS ECSTATIC to see Michael, and so excited over his deck of cards that it was difficult to get him calmed down long enough for any constructive work. Seeing the problems he was creating, Michael discreetly excused himself to accept the offer from an administrative aide for a tour of the hospital.

After Michael had left, Tony's session went marginally better, although he was still so preoccupied with his card tricks that Leslie found the only way to get his attention was to come up with some card games of her own. Unfortunately, her technique was not nearly as polished as Michael's, and Tony quickly grew bored. After half an hour, Leslie left Tony in the care of his speech pathologist, laughingly wishing the young woman better luck than she had had.

The afternoon went quickly, with Michael wandering in and out between patients to flash her a smile or to report on some of the antics of the children in the playroom, where he had quickly become a favorite. Leslie did not know why it should be, but there was a glowing feeling inside her simply knowing that Michael was near, that he was for once working with her instead of against her, that he found pleasure in what she did for a living, and that at any moment she could look up and find his tawny eyes gazing down at her.

It was late in the afternoon when her final patient left, and the administrative personnel had gone home for the day. A low thunder had begun to roll outside, splattering heavy drops of rain against the windows. The swollen sky outside was a deep and navy blue, contrasting the heavy shadow of gloom with the quiet, cozily lamplit interior of the administrative floor. Leslie's secretary, anxious to get home before the storm hit, hurried out behind the last patient, and for a moment Leslie was left alone with the distant sound of thunder and the patter of raindrops, taking a moment to glance over her case files before closing the office for the evening and going in search of Michael.

MICHAEL STOOD FOR A MOMENT in the doorway, drawn to the picture she made, unwilling to disturb it. A pool of lamplight fell over her shoulder, making a shimmering aura of her hair, illuminating a perfect circle upon the scattering of papers over her desk. Her head was bent studiously, her expression absorbed as she turned over a page. The angle of her neck was slim and long and sweet, inviting the touch of his fingers, the brush of his lips. The light illuminated the delicate transparency of her skin, the small nose, the lips long since devoid of lipstick, the shadowy arcs that her lashes fanned across her cheekbones. Behind her the purple force of the storm gathered and prepared to break, but inside all was serene. Watching her, he began to smile, softly and contentedly, without even being aware he was doing so.

"So," he said, coming into the room. "How's our little Tiger doing?"

Leslie looked up at the sound of his voice, closing the file with a rueful smile. "I don't know whether I should thank you or scold you for coming here today. Tony was pretty impossible." She shrugged, allowing her smile to widen into gentle appreciation. "But he was happy, and that's not such a common occurrence that we can overlook it. Thanks, Michael."

"I'm here to serve." He perched on the edge of her desk

while she gathered up her papers and shuffled them into her briefcase. His tone grew serious. "What's his prognosis, Leslie?"

Leslie looked up at him, something within her softening unpreventably toward this man, who could display such genuine concern for a child he had only met twice and for whom he bore no responsibility. She had to answer honestly, "Not very good, I'm afraid. The recovery rate for autistic children is not high, but we've made giant steps in just getting him to the point where he's no longer a danger to himself. By accepted standards, he's still a very disturbed little boy—but by his own standards we've seen monumental improvement. We have to be grateful for that."

Michael nodded slowly, almost reluctantly. "That's what I thought."

He looked wonderful today. His hair, softened by the day's rigor or the impending weather, was brushed in gentle sweeps away from his high forehead, glowing in the lamplight like muted gold. He was wearing a collarless pink shirt with tight elbow-length sleeves, and form-fitting white duck pants. Only he could manage to still exude masculinity in an outfit like that. The top three buttons of his shirt were undone, revealing the dip in his throat and several inches of the golden chest Leslie remembered so well, and the lean line of his hip was only inches from her arm. It took more concentration than was reasonably necessary for Leslie to keep her fingers from accidentally brushing over that hip as she went about the business of gathering up her papers.

"I've always thought," she continued, more to distract herself from the unwary course her thoughts were taking than anything else, "that if we could find some way to let him communicate with us half the problem would be solved. He has such a busy little mind, so much to express. But we've tried speech therapy, sign language—" she lifted her shoulders helplessly as she snapped her briefcase shut "—nothing seems to work."

Michael stood and walked over to the window, staring

out at the sluggish pattern of raindrops for a moment before he murmured thoughtfully, "Maybe he is."

Leslie got to her feet and picked up her briefcase. "What?"

Michael turned slowly. "Maybe he is communicating with us." His tone was very matter-of-fact, very reasonable, and to Leslie, totally baffling. "Do you ever make tapes of Tony's sessions?"

Leslie looked at him, a puzzled frown shadowing her eyes. "Well, yes. His speech pathologist does a lot of recording. Why?"

"Nothing." Michael's expression was completely shuttered, perfectly blank. "Just an idea. Do you think we could listen to some of them?"

Leslie hesitated, at a total loss. She couldn't begin to fathom what he was thinking, what he was planning, and it was impossible to read anything from his face or his tone. The rain was going to begin in earnest any minute and they really shouldn't waste any more time here if they didn't want to get caught in a real downpour. But something about him—perhaps it was no more than instinct on her part—told her that he *was* planning something, and her own curiosity couldn't let her walk away from it undiscovered. She led the way to the speech lab.

"Here we go," Leslie said, searching through the tape file. "Today's session. Tony was so excited about his cards I doubt whether Joanne got very far, but..."

She threaded the reel of tape through the machine and pressed the play button. Michael leaned back against Joanne's desk, his arm crossed, and listened.

"All right, Tony, that's wonderful...." Joanne's voice, clear and precise was drowned out at the end by Tony's high-speed chatter. "Yes, I love your card tricks, and I think you're a very smart little boy, but if we could just..." Tony's squeals rose in pitch, and Leslie smiled in sympathy with her colleague. "All right, Tony, show me the trick one more time." Tony began a feverishly incoherent diatribe that ended only when Michael strolled over and pushed the stop button.

"Well?" Leslie looked at him curiously—a look that quickly turned to suspicion as he began to rewind the tape, reversing the spools, adjusting playback speed and volume. "Now wait a minute, Michael, these are important medical records. Don't you dare try one of your cute tricks—"

He said simply, "Ssh," and engaged the tape.

The high-pitched blur of nonsense was Joanne's voice being played backward, following by another stream of Tony's jabber. Michael slowed the speed, and Joanne's voice came again.

And then Tony's voice, clear, unmistakable, perfectly coherent: "All right, Tiger, you are about to see one of the most incredible feats of prestidigitation ever known to man, last performed at the court of…"

Leslie felt the blood drain from her cheeks; astonishment registered like a shock wave in the center of her chest and blotted out even the sound of Tony's voice—that wonderful, incredible sound of Tony's voice speaking perfect English in clear, comprehensive tones.

"Michael." The whisper was barely audible through numbed lips and she gripped his arm with a force that caused her nails to dig into his flesh; he did not seem to notice. She stared at the machine. "Play it back. Do it again."

Quickly, Michael twisted knobs, pressed levers, and Tony's voice came again, reciting to the word the magician's patter Michael had given him that day on the boat.

She stared at Michael. He looked as stunned as she felt, his eyes fixed upon the machine that was playing back his own words to him in perfect detail and coming from a child experts had declared would never speak. It was no mistake. It was real. Tony was speaking, and he had been doing so all along. It was simply that no one had been listening.

Leslie's hand fluttered to her throat, as though to contain the wild, exuberant joy that was swelling there. Now it was she who couldn't speak, her head swimming, her eyes brimming, her heart performing a light dangerous rhythm in her chest that threatened to suffocate her with sheer wonder.

"Backward," Michael said. "He's been repeating everything he hears—only backward, and at high speed."

Something about his calm, matter-of-fact tone caused the bubble within her to explode, and she cried, "Michael!" Half laughing, half crying, dizzy with wild joy, she flung her arms around him. "Do you know what you've done? This is it, the clue we needed, the *chance* Tony needed."

His hands came up, startled, to cradle her waist; he looked down into her glowing, upturned face with a cautious wonder kindling in his own. "Is it? Do you think it will help?"

Leslie laughed and hugged him hard. "I think," she declared into the soft-hard warmth of his shoulder, "that you are a miracle worker after all!"

She felt the low rumble of his laughter within his chest as his arms tightened around her, his face pressed against her hair. "God, it just hit me. The kid was repeating every word I said! Now I'm trying to remember what I've said around him that I don't want him to repeat."

They looked at each other, faces awash with incredulous joy, eyes shining with wonder and hope, and alive with discovery. Between them was the shared thrill of a brush with the impossible, before them a world rich with possibilities. The moment was too intense for words, too intense even for a kiss. It was enough to simply look at each other and hold each other and share feelings that no one else could understand.

And then Michael declared, his eyes crinkling at the corners as his arms loosened the embrace, holding her lightly by the waist, "I think this calls for a celebration. How about a bottle of champagne at the best prime-rib house in town?"

Leslie laughed. "I'm up for that!"

"Leslie—" he looked at her anxiously "—will you be able to help Tony now? Do you think this will make a difference?"

Leslie's hands slid down his arms, and she felt such a surge of warmth and affection for him that it was like something warm and syrupy seeping through her pores, enfolding both of them in its honeyed glow. She held his hands and squeezed them tightly, smiling up at him. "It's a start, Michael," she said. "It's a start."

Chapter Ten

The restaurant Michael had chosen was in an unlikely location: on the second floor of a noisy, popular neighborhood tavern. "Not fancy," he had assured her with a wink, "just good." And he was right. It would have been uncomfortable, even awkward, if he had taken her to an overpriced, romantic little spot with dark corners and candlelight, violin music and fresh flowers. The understated, companionable atmosphere of this brightly-lit restaurant, which focused more on the quality of the food than the quality of the service, was exactly what was needed to keep the wonderful mood that had developed between them from becoming strained and self-conscious. It was easy to relax with Michael here, easier than she had ever known it could be.

Leslie, who generally hated to eat out, found the menu a cut above superb, everything prepared to succulent perfection. Even the champagne, surprisingly, was of a fine vintage, mellow and golden. By the time they poured the final glasses and ordered dessert, the excitement of their victory with Tony had leveled off to a warm, subtle glow of pleasure that felt to Leslie as though it would last forever.

She shook her head one last time in wonder of it all. "I'll schedule a conference with Joanne—the speech therapist—first thing in the morning. God, we have so much work to do." Her eyes sparkled like the bubbles in her glass as she looked at Michael. "I can't wait to see the look on Mrs. Swan's face. To think, the answer had been there all along...." And she shook her head again.

There was tenderness in Michael's smile, and also a measure of puzzlement. "I don't see how you do it—balance your career between the hospital and the Center. You seem to give everything you've got to each of them, yet they're at entirely opposite ends of the professional spectrum."

Leslie chuckled, and it was a light, throaty sound that generated small thrills of pleasure up Michael's spine. "That's a symptom of my schizoid tendencies, I suppose— the Center is a symbol of my rebellious streak, and the hospital a way to hold on to the last vestiges of my respectability." She sipped her champagne. "Actually, they're not so different as you might think. The mind, in whatever aspect, is a limitless challenge of the unknown, and I love each phase of my work equally."

"I can see that." The smile lingered in his eyes as their desserts arrived—a pineapple sorbet for Leslie, and fresh-fruit cup for Michael.

"Mmm, this is wonderful." Leslie sighed, dipping her spoon again into the frosty sorbet.

"I told you it would be. I've been known to drive all the way from Georgetown for one of Jason's meals—and I don't, as a rule, like to eat out. He even uses one or two of my recipes," he confided.

Leslie laughed. "So that's his secret!"

"So, what led you into this kind of work?" Michael asked after a moment, with interest.

"Well, as you probably know, my uncle started the Center." Michael nodded, and Leslie spooned up the last of the exquisite sorbet, letting the sensation linger on her taste buds. "My family," she continued, "has been into science in one form or another as far back as I can remember. Given my environment and heredity, I really didn't have too much choice in the matter of careers."

She pushed aside her dessert dish and picked up her

champagne glass, and she might have stopped there. But Michael knew there was more to her story and he waited patiently.

"My mother is a world-class genetic engineer," she went on in a moment, not knowing why she did except that it felt natural, almost a given, that she should unfold herself to him. "Besides being brilliant, gifted, highly respected and a great hostess, she is also beautiful. And such an obsession with details..." She smiled a little, reminiscently, but it was not a pleasant expression. It was very near a grimace, and hidden within it was the shadow in her eyes of unhappy years. "She fired a housekeeper one time when she found a handprint smudge on an end table right before a big party, and felt perfectly justified in doing it, too. She claimed that polishing furniture was the woman's job and there was no excuse for not doing it right. It was my handprint."

Leslie shrugged. "She is a busy woman and has to allocate a lot of authority; she expects everyone to be as perfect as she is. The price you pay for greatness, I suppose. She is allowed a few quirks." She met Michael's eyes with a light lift of her eyebrows that was half self-conscious, half defensive. "Unfortunately, I didn't inherit a single shred of her compulsion for neatness—or perhaps fortunately. Compulsive behavior is not an acceptable trait in a psychologist.

"My father," she continued after a sip of champagne, "the world-renowned cardiologist, pioneered the field of heart-transplant surgery. Saved countless lives. He's very dedicated, very demanding, very thorough, very proud of himself, and not a very pleasant person. My parents have the perfect marriage because each of them hardly notices the other until they read their names in the paper; then they're very pleased to share the applause. They were born to greatness, married greatness, achieved greatness, and were great at everything they did—except raising children."

A silence fell, and Michael felt a yearning uncoil within

him for the child she had been, the woman she had become. He wanted to hold her, protect her, soothe away the hurt and chase away the shadows from her eyes. What he did was stay silent and listen as she went on.

"My parents barely recognize psychology as an acceptable profession," she said, her smile again faint and dry. "Psychiatry, perhaps, but psychology is like an avocation to them, a hobby to keep me busy until I grow up. As for parapsychology... Well, I admit, I probably followed Uncle Albert's footsteps partially as a way to shock my parents into recognizing that I had a mind of my own, but once I began studying the field I was hooked. There's so much to be learned," Leslie said thoughtfully. "So many possibilities, so many challenges."

The rush of the storm made a soothing sound against the insulated walls and roof; the murmur of background conversation and the clink of silverware was bright and reassuring. Michael reached across the table and entwined her fingers with his. He smiled. "So now I know what makes the lady psychologist tick. I think there's more of your parents inside you than you realize, you know, despite the fact that you've done everything possible to be exactly the opposite of what they expect."

Leslie looked at him, surprised at his perception, then she relented with a smile and a shrug. "Like my pedantic attention for detail, my obsession with cold facts? The hardships of my upbringing, I suppose. As I said, the scientific tradition goes back for generations in my family."

"That must make it particularly difficult to practice in your chosen field, where so much depends on accepting the impossible without any proof at all—on blind faith alone."

Leslie laughed, though now the sound was a little nervous. "That's the very myth I'm trying to dispel. In parapsychology, as in any other field, if it can't be proven, it doesn't exist."

Michael said very softly, "And with so much to prove, you can't afford to take risks, can you?"

The gentle, probing understanding in his eyes told her

he was referring to more than just professional risks, and like so many basic truths, it sounded odd when it was put into words. Suddenly uncomfortable, Leslie withdrew her hand, smiling a little to cover her reasons, and sipped her champagne. "And what about you, Mr. Bradshaw? Do you have a family?"

He sat back, relaxing, allowing her the momentary evasion. "More or less," he answered. "I come from what is commonly known as a broken home. My parents fought until I was eighteen, then divorced as soon as I went to college. But—" he turned over the check and glanced at it absently "—you're off duty, and I won't put you to the trouble of analyzing the traumatic results of my unstable childhood."

Leslie tried to push down an irrational sense of disappointment, of bereavement, as he paid the check and escorted her out. She had shared more of herself with him tonight than she had with any man—more, certainly, than she had ever intended to. Didn't he realize how important it was to her that he respond in kind? But, as always, all he was willing to give her were bits and pieces, tantalizing clues and shadowy outlines that suggested, but did not complete, the puzzle that was Michael Bradshaw.

It was raining severely as they came out, and Leslie waited in the shelter of the eaves as Michael went to get the car. She felt a little guilty, for if he was going to get wet it seemed only fair that she should, too, but when she saw him in the interior light as she scooted from the protection of the building to the protection of the car, she was amazed.

"How did you do that?" she accused, tugging the car door closed behind her. "You're bone dry!" In the half-second she had been exposed to the downpour her slacks and blouse had been splotched with huge spatters of rain, but not a single droplet had touched Michael.

His eyes twinkled. "Umbrella?"

"You didn't leave with an umbrella," she argued, "and even if you had, your pants and shoes would be wet." She peered down at the long leg that rested near hers. "They're not."

He shrugged and put the car in gear. "Maybe I just ran between the raindrops."

Maybe it was the champagne, or maybe it was leftover exhilaration from the breakthrough at the hospital, but at that moment Leslie thought it was entirely possible that was what he had done.

Leslie's car was the only one in the parking lot when they arrived back at the Center. It looked forlorn and abandoned sitting beneath the muted glow of a streetlamp in the silvery downpour, very much like Leslie suddenly felt as she prepared to say good-night to Michael.

"This is silly, you know." He pulled up close to her car and turned off the engine. "Let me drive you home and I'll pick you up in the morning. There's no point in your driving in this mess."

The steady drum of rain on the roof of the car sounded unnaturally loud without the hum of the engine, but Leslie assured herself it sounded much worse than it was. Thunder was muffled in the distance, and a flash of lightning briefly illuminated Michael's face as he turned to her.

"I'm a perfectly competent driver," she told him. "Besides, it's letting up some now."

He reached out to crook an affectionate finger under her chin, his eyes soft and his tone teasing. "Not too much champagne?"

It had been a long time since anyone had worried about Leslie's safety. She liked it. "I'm fine," she assured him, and the warmth of his light touch on her chin brought luminosity to her eyes, tenderness to her smile. She could feel it traveling through her bloodstream like small dancing bubbles of wonder. "Good night, Michael," she said softly, but made no move to reach for the door. There was a light in his eyes that held her.

He kissed her. A breath, an embrace, and then she was melding with him, her arms around his neck, her lips opening beneath his, drinking of him, blending with him, being absorbed by him.

She knew there was a console between them, but their bodies were pressed together, stomach and chest, arms enfolding, mouths exploring. The rush of rain against the metal roof was like a sea tide, ebbing and flowing with the rhythm of Leslie's pulse, the emotions that ruled her. His hair was heavy and silky beneath her fingers; his breath filled her lungs, his taste becoming her own.

She could feel it, the hot surge of electricity that flowed between them, just as real and just as powerful as the lightning that flashed outside. It dizzied her; it weakened her; it left her helpless. Reality, in Michael's arms, was no more than a memory of what might have been, and nothing was left of Leslie except her need for him.

He lifted his lips slightly, tantalizing her with sweeps of his tongue across her lips and teeth while his thumb made lightly teasing circular motions over the material that covered her breast. She felt herself sinking into him, and she thought, *Nothing could be like this.... Nothing could be as wonderful as it is between us.*

Desire was such a steadily engorging, powerfully predetermined thing that she hardly felt its pain, for the promise of fulfillment was just as certain, just as natural. She and Michael, who were meant to be together, who were meant to be a part of each other... Decision had been taken out of her hands, and she could no more stop the inevitable between them than she could stem the torrent of rain outside.

His hands explored and caressed the shape of her breasts, lightly, maddeningly, while his lips clasped her throat and her neck and the sensitive hollow behind her earlobe. She thought she could surely die from pleasure, from wanting, from waiting for what so certainly must be theirs.

His hands went around her back, pressing her close; he kissed her with a ferocity of possession that left her dazed, breathless, every nerve in her body stripped and throbbing. And then he lifted his face; he loosened his embrace. When the world slowly reoriented itself and Leslie opened dazed and hungry eyes, he was looking down at her, his expression totally unreadable in the muted light that came through foggy, rain-streaked windows.

He smiled at her, and it seemed an effort. His breath was warm upon her heated cheek, his hand unsteady as it came up to smooth away a strand of her hair. "I like your hair," he said huskily, his eyes absorbed with the motions of his fingers, stroking the strands.

Leslie managed a breathless chuckle. "Dark roots and all?"

The sun lines around his eyes deepened slightly. "Dark roots and all."

Leslie's body was trying to make a frantic adjustment to this change of pace and was succeeding by degrees. Her heartbeat was still erratic, her breath still shallow, her limbs still weak. But thought was coming more clearly. She reached up a hand that was no more steady than Michael's own and laid it alongside his face. Instinctively, like a cat seeking stroking, he turned to the motion, rubbing his cheek against her palm.

"And I like your eyes," she whispered.

He brought both hands up to cup her face, looking at her with those wonderful, passion-darkened eyes, and though she could feel with every sense she possessed the struggle that was going on inside him, none of it showed on his face. "Leslie...love." Again, the effort to smile strained at his lips. His eyes searched her face, briefly, intensely, and then were still. "Just for the record, I could have you out of those clothes so fast you'd still be wondering how it happened when you're a gray-haired little old lady telling the tale to our grandchildren...." And again his eyes swept over her; when they returned to meet her own there was no longer any doubt of what he was seeing. His voice was quiet. "But you're still not sure of me, are you?"

Leslie's pulse had calmed; her breath was coming more easily now. But the fever still burned and the urgency still flared and for a moment all she could think was, *Yes, I'm sure. I'm sure I want you holding me, touching me, filling me, making magic inside me. And I want you now.*

But that, she knew, was not what he meant.

With a trembling breath, she let her hand fall from his face, resting it lightly against his shirtfront, just over the slow and steady beat of his heart. There was aching in her eyes as she looked at him, but also the tentative return of a measure of reason. She said with difficulty, "Michael... I can't help it. I—I don't know you, don't understand you...and everything that's logical within me tells me that you're bad for me, that nothing good will ever come from this...." *But I still want you, more than I've ever wanted anyone in my life*, she thought, but he did not give her a chance to say it.

His hand passed with one last stroking caress over the crown of her head. Slowly he moved away, though his hands drifted down to hold hers lightly. The longing in his eyes made Leslie want to bite her lip with the pain. "But that's the whole trick, Leslie," he said gently. "If relationships were easy, everybody would have one. You'll never know me, or understand me...until you can accept me on faith, just like that, no questions asked." He smiled, though it was a sad smile, and brushed his lips lightly across her cheek. "The magic only comes, you see, when you stop thinking about it. That's the secret."

And that, of course, was the one thing Leslie could not do.

She opened the door, and it had stopped raining. The storm did not resume until she was safe in her own bed, alone.

MICHAEL KNEW he wouldn't be able to sleep that night. A cold shower would do nothing to ease his feverish longing, for the ache he felt for her went far behind the physical. It had lodged itself in his very soul.

He couldn't believe he had let her walk away from him like that. He could be with her right now, wrapped in her arms, sleepy and satisfied, feeling the edge of passion beginning to build between them anew. She would be his, physically and emotionally, for as long as he wished to hold her.

Perhaps that was what had stopped him. When had he begun to want more from her? When had he begun to fear that what he really wanted from her was forever?

All of Michael's life he had been ruled by his instincts, and now his instincts suddenly terrified him. There was no place in his life for a woman, especially a woman like Leslie. She was right to be cautious. Thank God she was cautious.

The cabin seemed small and claustrophobic, the steady pound of rain on the deck overhead sealing him in. He paced restlessly, pausing once to idly flip through a book, then tossing it down again with a dry grimace. Houdini. Even he couldn't have come up with a way to get out of this one.

At last he flung himself down on top of the made bed, staring up at the ceiling. Michael was used to being the controller, the manipulator of imaginations, minds, reality, but most especially of his own destiny. For the first time in his life he was in a situation he could not control, for the woman who had no place in his life had already carved out a place for herself in his heart, and there was not a thing he could do about it.

At last, with a sigh, he picked up a magazine, knowing he could do nothing to bring sleep, hoping he could distract his mind. A full-page color advertisement invited him to tropical paradise, where he would enjoy the wonder and romance of the "longest pink-sand beach in the world." Gentle Caribbean waters lapped at the rosy beach, a turquoise sky gleamed overhead, a lush palm tree swayed in the foreground. He imagined sailing there with Leslie, first stop on their trip around the world. He imagined her in a form-fitting swimsuit and some kind of gauzy white cover-up, her skin glinting goldenly against the brilliance of the sun, her eyes laughing up at him. He imagined her hand, warm and secure, entwined with his as they walked along the beach; and later, in some private cove, they would drop to the ground and make love while tropical breezes caressed their skin and the sound of the ocean whispered like a love song in the distance. He imagined the sensation of belonging to her, and she to him, forever.

And then, with a small groan, he covered his eyes with his forearm and tried not to wish so hard.

THE STORM WHIPPED AND RAGED outside, sounding now like a screaming cat, now like a growling boar, now gathering with the thundering hoofbeats of a charging bull...and then abruptly retreating, backing off and waiting.

"Upstairs, the woman slept alone, warm and dry and lost in her dream. Downstairs, the plop-plop of a slow trickle of rain that seeped in through the loosely sealed basement window was steady and hypnotic. It was dark there, smelling of mildew and old shoes and something else, something faint and foul and not quite dead....

"From the corner a slow, sucking, slithering sound uncoiled against the dusty cement floor. Blind white eyes opened, closed lidlessly, and opened again. Its narrow fleshy body quivered with sensation, with need, with hunger. It began to move, leaving a glistening slimy trail in its wake as it inched across the floor toward the steps, upward, and upward...."

Leslie let the book fall closed upon her chest, unable to concentrate. A forlorn breath hissed through her teeth as she stared bleakly up at the ceiling. What was she doing here in bed alone?

The rain on the roof had an empty, tinny sound, reminding her by contrast how powerful it had sounded, and how secure she had felt when she was in Michael's arms, sealing them inside their own separate world. Why had he stopped? Why had he given her a chance to think? She knew, as surely as she had ever known anything, that if he hadn't made her deliberately pause and think about what she was doing, she would be in his arms right now, wrapped in his nakedness, savoring the magic.

He had wanted her to be sure; he had given her a choice. And Leslie was not at all certain she was happy with the decision she'd made. Concise, rational Leslie, who could never love a man without analyzing him thoroughly beforehand, who could never trust a man like Michael Bradshaw, who by his very nature was as ephemeral as the lightning that flashed across her windowpane. Leslie, who knew with every particle of logic in her mind that sleeping with him would be more than just an act of passion, and who had no intention of ever allowing it to become anything more, who knew better than to believe in him but was rapidly losing the battle to remember why.... She couldn't be falling in love with him. To do so would be against every rational law of relationships she had ever known. And Leslie, so precise, so cautious, with so much to prove, could not afford to make a mistake like that.

At last, with a heavy sigh, she reached over to turn off the light, drawing the covers up to her ears to smother the sound of the lonely storm. She fell asleep wondering what Michael was doing, and she dreamed of walking hand in hand with him on a beach covered with pink sand.

some scrambled faded text at the top of the page partially visible

Chapter Eleven

Leslie stood at the door of the laboratory for a moment, watching Michael. He was sitting at the worktable in the center of the room, a preoccupied scowl on his face, turning a block of wood over and over in his hands. On the television screen before him a videotape of the Gaynor twins demonstrating their fire-making ability played.

Leslie said, smiling, "You can't figure it out, can you?"

He glanced at her and replied absently, "No." The troubled look didn't leave his eyes. "No, I can't." He got up and walked over to the machine, staring at the blank screen for a moment after he had disengaged the tape. "Fire is not an easy illusion, I'll admit, but it can be done. They're just not doing it in any way that *I've* ever seen before."

"You just won't admit it," Leslie said, working hard at keeping the smugness out of her tone. "You won't admit that you can't find anything because there is nothing *to* find. The twins aren't hiding anything. They're not deceiving anyone. They have genuine psychic power that they can't explain any more than you can."

Michael tilted his head, fastening her with a peculiarly curious, half-amused gaze. "Since when did you start believing in miracles?"

Leslie was a little taken aback, not only by the question, but by the warm, easy light she saw kindling in his eyes. She had spent the last two working days at the hospital in intensive consultation with all the professionals involved in Tony's therapy, and she had not seen Michael. She had missed those eyes.

But his question made her uncomfortable, and she didn't feel like thinking about it right now. She said, dismissing it with a shrug, "Maybe you've been working on the problem too hard; you need a break. How would you like to go visit a haunted house?"

His light brows arched appreciatively. "With you? Darling, lead the way."

The wonderfully suggestive, lightly teasing twitch of his lips sent a tiny thrill of delight through Leslie. How could she possibly have missed anyone so much in such a short space of time?

"We've been monitoring a report of poltergeist activity," she explained as they left his lab. "The family has gone away for a few weeks." She grimaced. "Probably to get away from the stress more than anything else. Anyway, they've agreed to let us set up our equipment in their house while they're gone. The technician who usually does this sort of thing is sick, and I just need you to help me unload the equipment and carry it into the house. I can do the rest. It shouldn't take more than an hour."

"Any little thing I can do." His hand fell quite naturally on her waist as they stepped out into the bright, heated day. Leslie thought she was almost growing accustomed to the feel of his fingers there, as though they belonged. "Tell me about Tony. I haven't seen you in a couple of days; I figured you were busy at the hospital."

"Oh, Michael." She turned to him excitedly, her eyes glowing as they always did when she thought about Tony. "I wish you could have seen the expression on his mother's face when I told her what you'd found! And the consultation team—they couldn't believe it! We're thinking about doing a paper on it. You don't know what possibilities this opens up."

She began to explain to him about the brain's mirror image and the theories that explained Tony's peculiar method of speech, the possible therapies that could be tried, similar cases in the past. The road to rehabilitation would be long and there was no guaranteed success rate, but now that the problem was diagnosed they at least had a chance, which was more than they had ever had before.

By the time she paused for breath, they had loaded the last of the equipment into the Center's van and Michael, taking the driver's seat, had pulled out of the parking lot. She caught herself, abashed. "Sorry," she said. "I didn't mean to gush. But things like this happen so rarely—it seems you can work a lifetime, really, without getting a single break—and when it does happen it's a high like you wouldn't believe."

Michael smiled at her, warmth crinkling his eyes and softening his face. "I like to see you gush." Then, indicating the road, "Which way?"

She gave him simple directions to a nearby suburban neighborhood, and when he parked the van on the tree-lined street in front of a very ordinary brick ranch-style house he looked at her dubiously. "This is it? It doesn't look very haunted to me."

"Atmosphere only comes with Hollywood," she replied flippantly, and clambered out of the van. "And hauntings are where you find them."

She used the key on loan to her by the owners to unlock the deadbolt and disengage the security system, and she and Michael carried the carefully packed video and audio equipment, piece by piece, into the living room, then reset the alarm. "The Elliots are just your average American family," she explained after their last trip to the van. "Husband, wife, son aged three and daughter aged twelve. The house is only five years old. A couple of months ago they began to experience unusual phenomena—furniture moving around, lamps flying through the air, broken dishes, things like that. It's pretty scary, I gather."

She set her box of cameras on the pumpkin-colored wall-to-wall carpeting and dusted off her hands. The Elliots had not left the air conditioner on, and it was hot inside. Her clothes were beginning to stick to her, and she lifted the heavy hair off the back of her neck.

"We've had seismologists and geologists in," she continued, kneeling to unpack the cameras, "even a meteorologist to examine the effects of changing atmospheric conditions. No fault line, no underground rivers, no peculiar weather pockets. We've checked the house for structural faults, and even called in the power company to investigate possible electrical surges. Sometimes you can get a sonic-echo effect from nearby railroads or air-traffic patterns—but that's been ruled out, too. The only thing left to do now is to see what kind of effects we can catch on film—without the possibility of human intervention."

Michael sat back on his heels, impressed. "Very thorough," he complimented her. "So what's your theory?"

Leslie shrugged. "There have been cases like this when paranormal disturbances center around a pubescent child—usually female. The Elliots' twelve-year-old daughter. Some people think adolescence causes an increase in brain-wave activity that can manifest itself by disturbing physical objects, although it's just as likely that the child is actually doing these things, subconsciously, by very physical means, in order to get attention. She's probably not even aware of what she's doing. I've talked to her, and she seems just as upset by all of this as the rest of the family."

Michael shook his head slowly, laughing softly. "I do wish you'd make up your mind which direction you're going in. One minute you're on my case for trying to find a rational explanation for the activities of the Gaynor twins; the next you're telling me all about how there can't be anything but a rational explanation for poltergeists. Don't you ever commit to anything?"

It was an innocent comment; there was surely not reason for it to go straight to her heart like a cold accusing finger. She looked at him for a moment of confusion and awful vulnerability, and when she saw his eyes soften she knew she had revealed too much in her own. She said quickly, turning back to the unpacked cases, "Let's get this equipment set up."

Michael was interested and attentive as she explained the placement of time-lapse cameras, video equipment that would be activated by the slightest movement, sound or temperature change, monitors that would relay unusual activity back to the Center, and supersensitive audio recording devices that would pick up high and low sonic impulses inaudible to the human ear.

"Pretty sophisticated stuff," he commented admiringly.

Leslie nodded, consulting the placement diagram given her by the technician. "And the way we've got everything placed, there won't be a single strategic point not under surveillance of some sort at every minute." She placed a small probelike device on one of the camera stands as indicated by the diagram. "Even ultrasensitive thermometers, which will register a fraction of a change in temperature. The Elliots," she confided with a noncommittal shrug, "claim they feel a cold draft sometimes, just before the phenomena begin."

Michael watched as she lifted her hair again, causing her breasts to thrust against the material of her shirt. He could see the lacy outline of her bra, the glistening triangle of skin beneath the top two unfastened buttons, and it was hard to swallow. It was hard to move his eyes away, even when she flashed him a negligent smile and commented, "I wouldn't mind one of those cold drafts right now."

Leslie saw the unexpected intensity in Michael's eyes, and it communicated some subliminal message to her that made her heart beat faster. Quickly she averted her gaze and nodded to the two remaining cases on the floor. "We'll set those up in the rec room," she said, "and then we'll be finished."

The recreation room was on the basement level, and a little cooler. Like the rest of the house it was typical suburbia, the place where the average American family went to relax at the end of a long day. There was a long plaid sofa, some scattered plastic chairs, a few bean bags. A pool table dominated the center of the room, and a convertible ping-pong and card table was folded against one wall. There were video games and board games stacked on the shelves, a wide-screen television set and a stereo, a wet bar in one corner. It was the furthest thing from the stereotypical haunted house.

Leslie chattered cheerfully as Michael helped her set up the cameras in the two far corners, feeling the urge to keep the conversation going purely as a protective device. She had not imagined it would be so difficult to be around him again, to catch that sweet-spicy scent of his cologne at odd moments, to hear the teasing smile in his voice, to watch the deft movements of his hands at work. Everything he did made her wonder why she had been so cautious, so determined, so reluctant with him...and why she had been so foolish as to insist upon seeing him again today.

"We'll flip the switches as we leave," Leslie said, fussing with a control knob on one of the cameras, "and leave things undisturbed for a few days before we come back to check the data—if any—that's been collected."

Michael's hand fell very lightly against the back of her neck, causing her to repress a startled leap of her nerves. She hadn't realized he was standing so close. "Why are you so nervous?" he asked softly. She could sense the smile playing with his lips as he suggested, "Are the poltergeists getting to you?"

"Don't be silly." She knew she should step away from the light, tantalizing caress of his fingers against her hair, silk against silk upon the sensitive flesh at the back of her neck. She kept her voice very nonchalant. "What makes you think I'm nervous?"

"You always talk like a scientist when you're nervous—or defensive."

And then he stepped away, leaving her feeling bereft, confused and impatient with herself. He was right; she was on edge, and he knew exactly why. She didn't like feeling like a confused, incompetent adolescent, and that was exactly the way he made her feel. She didn't like not being able to cope with her own feelings. *Oh, Michael*, she thought with a sort of distant, resigned despair, *how long are we going to let this go on? Isn't it time we both faced some truths about ourselves?*

But a long time ago he had put control into her hands, and she knew she would have to make the first move. She realized to her dismay that she didn't want the responsibility. She wanted him to take her into his arms and sweep her away on a tide of that mind-stripping magic she knew so well; she wanted to think with her instincts, her body, her heart and not with her mind. She wanted to avoid the responsibility for a decision that could open her up to more hurt and disillusionment than she had ever known. She didn't have the courage to take that step of unquestioning trust that would be required to make herself so willingly vulnerable.

But to do that would be to cheat Michael and herself. He deserved more than that.

Michael had wandered over to the opposite corner to check the tape recorder there. Leslie turned to look at him, clasping her hands before her; she took a breath. "Michael, could we talk for a minute? I think—" She broke off at a sudden gust of cold wind that swept past her.

He looked up, startled. "Did you feel that?"

And, instantaneously, the door to the basement swung closed with a loud crash that made Leslie jump back a little and stifle a cry, staring at the sealed exit.

"What the hell—" Michael frowned and started toward the stairs, Leslie pressing close behind.

"They must have left a window open upstairs somewhere," she rationalized quickly, though her heart was still pounding in her chest and she had to restrain a very great urge to clutch Michael's arm, just like a heroine in an old Gothic movie.

"We checked all the windows," Michael replied absently, and turned the doorknob. It wouldn't budge.

He lifted an eyebrow. "Did the wind also twist the lock from the outside?"

Leslie stared at him. "What?" Quickly, she pushed past him, rattling the doorknob futilely. "It's locked!" she exclaimed.

"I believe I just pointed that out," Michael murmured, and stepped back.

"But how could that happen?" she demanded. "I don't see a lock anywhere." She put her shoulder against the door and shoved, turning the doorknob at the same time.

"I told you, it's a twist-lock deadbolt on the outside. Bruising your shoulder isn't going to help, Leslie." He pulled her gently away.

"How do you know what kind of lock it is?" She was unable to keep the suspicion out of her eyes or her voice, and his eyes began to sparkle mildly as he noticed.

"Locks are a, er, hobby of mine," he confessed. "I always notice them."

Leslie leaned back against the narrow wall, a hiss of frustrated breath escaping through her teeth. "Very cute, Bradshaw. You only scared me out of ten years' growth. Now if you don't mind—" She gestured meaningfully to the door.

The look of innocence he returned was dancing with amusement. "What makes you think I had anything to do with this?"

"Oh, come on, Michael! This is not a dusty storeroom in a building filled with people. This is someone else's house, and it's not a bit funny! The joke is over. Let's get out of here."

Michael lifted his hand gravely. "Upon my honor, Leslie, this was *not* my doing."

At the top of the stairs, with the light coming from below her, Leslie saw the shadows cast upon his angular face and the gleaming amber eyes that made him look more than a little satyric—and not at all trustworthy. But more than that, in the narrow confines of the stairwell, where it was impossible to stand side by side without touching, when his subtle, tantalizing scent seemed to wrap itself around her and his presence penetrated her pores and the very awareness of him was a palpable thing, it was very hard to think clearly. It was hard *not* to believe him.

Focusing on her common sense, she scowled. "So what's your explanation? Poltergeists?"

He looked thoughtfully at the locked door. "Maybe."

She released another exasperated breath. "Oh, for heaven's sake, will you just open it?"

He looked at her blankly. "How?"

"The same way you locked it!"

And now a faint impatient scowl skated across his features. "I told you, I *didn't* lock it. Be reasonable—how could I have? I was downstairs when the door slammed, and the lock is on the *outside*."

But Leslie was in no mood to be reasonable. Neither, she could tell, was arguing with him going to solve the problem, so she shrugged, dismissing it. "Okay, okay, so you didn't do it. But I'm sure you have a trick or two up your sleeve to undo it. Come on, Michael, we've got to get out of here."

Michael looked at her then at the door, dryly. "Sorry. I seem to have left my lock-picking kit in my other suit."

And then, as her lips compressed in a grim warning, he relented with a sigh. "We could try to loosen the hinges, I suppose. Go back down and see if you can find any kind of tools."

Leslie hurried downstairs to search, only to discover that the Elliots kept a very organized house. Nothing was in the recreation room except recreational equipment—not a screwdriver, hammer, or tool of any kind, not even a fingernail file. At last, sitting on the floor and looking around in dismay, she suggested hopelessly, "What about a pool cue?"

Michael came down the stairs. "It doesn't matter; we probably wouldn't be able to budge those hinges anyway. They seem to be pretty much painted to the frame."

"Great." Leslie leaned back against the wall and drew her knees up to her chest, looping her arms around them.

"What do we do now? There's not even a telephone down here."

Michael dropped gracefully to the floor beside her. "Wait until someone misses us, I guess—or until the poltergeists decide to let us go."

Leslie looked at her watch. "Everyone at the Center has gone home by now. Nobody will miss us until tomorrow. Oh, for heaven's sake, this is the most ridiculous thing that has ever happened to me!" And she fixed a death-dealing glare on Michael. "I swear to God, Michael, if you had anything to do with this..."

"I *told* you I didn't," he replied, with more impatience in his tone than she had ever heard him use before. "Would it be too much to ask that you take my word for something, just once?"

Leslie looked away, somewhat chagrined, considering this. And then, hesitantly, a dread new idea came into her mind. "Michael..." she said cautiously, turning back to him, "if you didn't do it, then do you suppose...someone entered the house while we were down here? Someone who's—" she swallowed hard "—still up there?"

The annoyance on his face gentled into sympathetic reassurance and he pointed out, "You turned the alarm system back on when we came in, didn't you? And besides, we would have heard footsteps overhead if anyone was moving around upstairs." His arm slipped around her shoulders, half playful, half comforting, and his fingers tugged lightly at a lock of her hair. "Face it, love, for this once there *is* no natural explanation."

Leslie sat there for a moment, adjusting as much to the wonderfully secure sensation of Michael's arm around her, his fingers threading gently through her hair, as to the possibilities his words evoked. How much easier it was to believe him than to doubt him when he held her like this. His touch, however casual, seemed to have the power to mesmerize her thinking mind as well as her body's responses, and it was not, she realized for the first time, such a bad thing. It was a simple matter of letting go, and in a situation as hopeless as this, there didn't seem much point in doing anything else.

Oh, Michael, she thought, letting her head rest easily and naturally on his shoulder, *how much you've been asked to tolerate from me.*

She glanced up at him, a little uncertainly. "I'm sorry," she said, and it felt strange to say those words. "For accusing you of locking us in, I mean. I guess..." And she glanced down at the two hills of her knees, pulled close against her chest. She forced a crooked smile. "I guess I don't make much sense sometimes. I mean, here I have dedicated my career to investigating the supernatural, but I refuse to believe it when it hits me right in the face." Then, thoughtfully, "I wish we had turned on those cameras upstairs."

He laughed softly. His fingers trailed a wonderfully teasing path across the back of her neck, making her skin prickle all the way down to her toes. "Actually, I'm not finding it so easy to believe, either. I'm just as much a skeptic as you are...maybe more so." His voice grew thoughtful. "Just like you, I want to believe in what I can't explain, I think, but can never quite bring myself to do it." She felt the smile in his voice, the slight lift of his shoulders, and his finger lightly, teasingly, outlining the shape of her ear. "So I compensate by making magic with mirrors and invisible wires; you fill your bookshelves with paperback horror novels, and neither of us is willing to believe what's right in front of our eyes."

His hand left her neck, drifting down her arm, to her waist, where it rested lightly, as though he knew he should break the intimacy but couldn't bring himself to do it. Leslie looked at him, her eyes still and waiting, and she saw in his eyes the same kind of hesitance, the wonder and the wanting, that seemed to have her entire being in its grip.

He said softly, searching her face, "The trouble is, Les, that if you don't believe in anything, you can't commit to anything...." His lashes fell, shading those all-too-revealing eyes; his smile was a little forced, his voice strained. "Damn," he said lowly. "We're so much alike it's spooky." He looked at her. "Sooner or later one of us is going to have to take the plunge."

It was as simple as that. All her life she had been looking for miracles, for magic, but was afraid to see them even when they crossed her path. Michael had come into her life and forced her to take a stand, without meaning to, without her even knowing it. Believing was not a matter of will, but a matter of instinct, and she knew she'd been running from her instincts too long. If she didn't make the move now, the magic might never come into her life again.

Leslie lifted her hand and placed it lightly alongside Michael's face. His lashes flew up, his eyes met hers with a cautious lightening and darkening of pleasure and question that he could not hide. She whispered, "I want to believe in you, Michael." And she kissed him, softly.

His arms slid around her; her legs lowered to allow her body freer access to his as he drew her closer, as the kiss deepened. The fireworks started in her head, the wonderful celebration of freedom, and she drank of him, gloried in him, gave herself over completely to him and what they made together.

He lifted his face, and through the haze of her own passion she caught a blur of his flushed face and bright eyes before he buried his lips in her neck. "Leslie," he whispered hoarsely, "don't tease me. My self-control is not what it used to be."

"I'm not." She let her trembling fingers slip inside his shirt, testing the damp, heated flesh and the straining muscles there, and his low moan was smothered in her neck. "I want you, Michael. I have—from the beginning...."

She felt the floor beneath her, Michael's body sheltering her. His hand tightened upon her scalp, tilting her face up to his, and what she saw in his eyes was the same wonder that radiated through her in shimmering waves of tenuous joy...those eyes, those beautiful, gentle, soul-seeing eyes, the first thing she had loved about him. Yet he whispered, "Leslie, are you sure? I want you to be sure."

Even now he wouldn't rush her. Even now he allowed her the rational thought that he knew was so important to her. But this wasn't a matter of rationality, and she had always known it. It was a matter of emotion. "Yes." She linked her hands around the back of his neck and brought him down to her. "I'm sure of what I feel."

Michael closed his eyes, drifting into the magic that was more powerful than any he had ever known or imagined. For this time it was real, and the one thing he had been waiting for all his life.

It built between them like a storm, signaled first by gentle lightning on the horizon, followed by low stirring tremors of thunder, gathering in magnetic impulses that sang through the air and dazzled the senses. Her clothes were gone and so were his; his smooth magnificent length stretched above her. She tasted the salt on his skin, cupped the heaviness of his hair in her fingers. She traced the tautness of muscles that flowed from his straining shoulders to the flatness of his back to his buttocks and the lean flanks below, and an urgency of need built in her throat, seared her skin. His lips teased her breasts and his tongue traced a shallow pattern down the center of her abdomen, which drew a gasping cry from her.

Sparks of dizzied electricity and fevered need danced between them, yet there was no desire to prolong the pleasure, no skillful design to tease or tantalize. He lifted his head; she looked into eyes that flamed with such longing and wonder that they seemed to consume her soul. She lifted herself to him and he entered her with a swiftness of possession that took her breath away, yet with such a surety of nature that tears of joy sprang to her eyes and she held him tighter and tighter.

And then the storm reached its peak. Distant was the sound of harsh breathing, the white-hot fusion of flesh to flesh, the taste of need that was sharp and sweet. Their movements were a desperate rhythm, the strength of their bodies driven by the weakness that bound them together. She saw visions, blinding bright colors and wisping phantoms of glory; she tasted Michael in her pores, her mind, her very soul. And when the storm broke it began with gentle ripples inside her that swelled into huge, breath-robbing cascades of which Michael was the essence, and in all the world, in all the universe, there was nothing but him.

"I love you...."

Had the whispered words been hers, or his? Heavily, Leslie lifted a hand to stroke his dampened hair. Her skin felt disassociated from the rest of her body, lightning-purged and tingling, a memory of collective electrons that wasn't quite real. His heart, pressed against hers, beat with such a rapid, unsteady rhythm that it throbbed throughout her body, joining them still. His breath flowed in a jerky stream across her heated skin, and she thought he couldn't have spoken, that it must have been her and she felt no shame for the words, no regret, only a wonderful rightness, the deep and abiding peace that comes with the truth. Perhaps, she thought hazily, no one had spoken at all, and the whisper had been no more than a mutual thought shared within their minds.

She never knew when Michael lifted his weight from her. She didn't feel the gentle kiss he placed upon her cheek or the strong arms that lifted her and carried her to the sofa. She slept, but she didn't dream, for dreams would be disappointing after the reality they had just shared together.

LESLIE AWOKE with the softness of sofa cushions against her cheek, the thin material of her own blouse covering her like a blanket. There was no disorientation, no wondering where she was or how she had gotten there, for the memory was beautifully clear, wondrously vibrant. A lazy, contented smile curved her lips—partially with the resonant joy for what they had discovered, partially with amusement for the time and place in which they had chosen to do it—and without opening her eyes, she reached out for Michael. When she didn't find him, she was forced to sit up and look around.

The first thing she noticed was that the door was open.

She stared at it for a long time, and she watched as before her very eyes the mystical, magical moment they had shared dissolved into nothing more than a dirty joke. Michael, who always had one more trick up his sleeve, who loved to catch her off guard, an integral part of whose charm was his deftness with illusion... Why had she thought he would stop now? What had ever made her believe that he would take what had happened between them any more seriously than he took anything else in his life?

Her throat tightened; woodenly she began to pull on her clothes. Just then Michael appeared at the top of the stairs. His smile went straight to her heart and she had to turn away from him stiffly as she stepped into her slacks.

He descended the stairs, and she could hear the note of caution in his voice that went beyond the warm pleasure of seeing her. "Damnedest thing," he said. "I didn't even hear the door open—I just looked up and there it was. I can't figure out how it happened."

Leslie clenched her teeth together to hold back a vicious, stinging retort. What had she expected from him, anyway? She knew what kind of man he was; he had never pretended to anything more, and that was precisely why she had been so careful not to get involved with him—because she knew she could never predict what he was going to do next. *But damn it, Michael, don't lie to me about it. Not now.*

She forced a button through its too-small buttonhole with fingers that were shaking and clumsy, and then she felt his hand lightly upon her shoulder. She jerked away as though stung.

"Leslie?" There was hesitance in his voice, and uncertainty. "Leslie, what's wrong?"

"Nothing." She forced an almost normal tone to her voice, working the buttons. What a stupid thing to get upset about. So he had gone to elaborate lengths to accommodate his plans for seduction. Didn't most men? And he hadn't exactly taken an unwilling woman. So what if he had exaggerated the circumstances a bit and enhanced the effect with trickery? He had only allowed her to believe what she wanted to believe, after all.

She said, hastily tucking her blouse into her pants and turning with a calm, composed smile, "We should be going. It's late, and I haven't had dinner yet."

The slow softening of his features as he reached for her was almost his undoing. His shiny, bouncing hair was tousled and unkempt, his shirt unbuttoned and untucked, his eyes soft and drowsy. "We'll go back to the boat. We'll make dinner, and—"

With all the strength of will she possessed, she stepped away just as his hand brushed her arm. "No, thanks, Michael," she said politely, turning to pick up her purse. "I think I'll just pick up something on the way home."

She couldn't have winded him more effectively if she had struck him in the stomach with a heavy object. What kind of game was she playing? After what had just happened between them, she was able to get up and walk so coolly away, as though it had been nothing to her—less than nothing. Even as the anger clenched in the muscles of his jaw and the long tendons of his arms, he saw a little deeper. No, he knew Leslie better than that. Of course it had meant something to her, as much, perhaps, as it had to him. But she was frightened, and when she was frightened she got defensive. But damn it, couldn't she see he was frightened, too? He was just as vulnerable, just as open to hurt, just as uncertain as she was. He had *asked* her to be sure.

He said, very quietly, "Leslie, what's wrong? Talk to me."

Oh, Michael, don't… She looked at him, so gentle, so sincere, and it didn't matter what he had done, or why he had done it, or even that he had lied about it. All she wanted to do was brush her hand over his rumpled hair, to soothe away the troubled lines from around his eyes, to press her face against his bare chest and to hold him and have him hold her.

"It doesn't matter," she mumbled uncomfortably and moved toward the door.

His hand snatched out so fast she didn't even see it coming until her wrist was held in his firm, steely grasp and he had twisted her around to face him. There was a blaze of dark color in his eyes and a cold, compressed anger to the set of his mouth that frightened her as much as his sudden movement had done.

And then, abruptly, as he saw the alarm spring to her face, he dropped her wrist, his hand clenching and unclenching by his side. He said, with a deadly forced calm, "Tell me. What have I done? Why are you acting this way?"

"Oh, for heaven's sake, Michael," she burst out suddenly, having no intention of making any sort of statement at all but finding herself suddenly unable to stay silent. "This!" She gestured sharply toward the open door, and she felt the hateful, angry sting of tears in her eyes. "You could have had me any number of times in any number of places these past few weeks—all it took was a twist of your wrist, a little razzle-dazzle and presto! Instant seduction! But why did it have to be here, now—with all this talk of poltergeists—in someone else's house! It was...cheap." And with the last word her voice trailed off into what she hoped desperately was not a sob, for even as she heard herself speak she writhed inside with shame.

He looked at her in plain disbelief, and underscoring it, far in the back of his eyes, a guarded hurt. "You think," he said slowly, "that I arranged all this, that I deliberately locked you in here with me and then lied about it just so I could make love to you? I would have thought," he said slowly, looking at her as though he didn't even know her, "that you would have at least given me credit for more class than that."

Immediately as the words were out she knew how ridiculous it was, and how low an accusation she had flung at him. Her cheeks scorched miserably and she couldn't look at him. She felt again like a clumsy child, irrational, incompetent, oversensitive.

She took a shaky breath. "No, Michael. I'm the one who lacks class, to even say such a thing."

He stepped backward, leaning his shoulders against the wall, hands in his pockets, looking at her.

"I—I'm sorry." She made herself meet his gaze, swallowing uncomfortably. "It was a stupid thing to say, to think. I—I guess I'm just so used to being—"

"Suspicious," Michael supplied for her quietly, and she nodded.

"Michael, I never intended..." She started to say "to fall in love with you," but something in his very remote, carefully guarded expression stopped her. She looked at him helplessly. "Don't you see, Michael? None of this makes sense to me. Being with you is like being in a whirlwind, and none of the natural laws of physics apply. I can't deal with things I don't understand and—well, I guess it threw me for a minute and I reacted badly. I didn't mean to lash out at you."

He regarded her steadily. "Do you still think I tricked you?"

She swallowed on a thickening throat. "Actually—" she looked at him hesitantly "—I'm the one who invited you to come with me. I think I knew even then why. I didn't intend for it to happen like this...." She gestured helplessly to the door, to the room. Her eyes met his again, steadily. "But...I'm not sorry it happened."

His face softened, and with it, everything in Leslie's heart. He stepped forward; he took both her hands in his. "We still have a way to go, don't we, Les?" he inquired gently.

She nodded.

He took a deep breath, and brought one of her hands to his lips. He brushed it lightly with a kiss, then laid her knuckles gently against his face. His eyes were velvet soft, heavy with thought. "You know," he said simply, "that this thing between us isn't going to be so easy to walk away from, don't you?''

Again she nodded. Perhaps that was what frightened her most.

"Come home with me," he persuaded her softly.

She knew if she did that she would never leave. She shook her head slowly. "I'd better not. I have to drive to Washington tomorrow to have dinner with my father, and I should get some sleep tonight." She dropped her eyes briefly, and then met his again. She opened her hand against his face, caressing the smooth, golden plane a final time, hoping he would understand. "I need some time, Michael," she said simply.

The emotions that raced through his eyes in shades of light and dark were too swift and too complex for her to catch. Then he kissed her fingers again, lightly, and released her hands. His voice was sober. "I'm afraid this time thinking isn't going to help you much, Les."

She realized that. But she didn't know what else to do.

Chapter Twelve

Leslie worked at the hospital the next day, and Michael made no attempt to contact her. Leaving her alone to think this through was the last thing in the world he wanted to do—he had learned by now that nothing but trouble came from Leslie's thinking—but it was something he had to do. For Michael there were no doubts, but Leslie would never be comfortable with herself, or with him, or with their relationship, until she had applied the test of rationality to something that couldn't be analyzed.

He knew what a chance he was taking. She could very easily look at things with that logical, objective mind of hers and reach the only possible logical conclusion, and armed with that strength, she could turn and walk out of his life forever. The possibility made his palms grow clammy. Of course it made no sense. Of course it wouldn't be easy. Love never was.

He knew better than anyone how difficult it was to give blind trust, to make a commitment to something that had never been proven to exist before. His own home life had taught him cynicism at an early age, and he had spent the rest of his life proving to himself over and over again that all intangibles were an illusion. And Leslie, so much of what she knew about herself depended on that cautious, pedantic nature of hers. He shouldn't expect her to take a risk like the one that would be required to love him.

But that kind of risk was the only thing that would make their relationship worth having.

For a time last night she had opened herself to him completely, she had believed in him instinctively, she had trusted him without question. And miracles had happened. But the moment she had realized what she had done, the old instinctive defenses began to surface; she backed away, throwing up armor of doubt and insecurity, hiding behind her shield of rationality, refusing to believe that the impossible could come to be. Her wariness and her skepticism ran deep, and couldn't be overcome by a single night of passion. But until she could accept him completely, just as he was—until she could believe in him unquestioningly, until she was willing to realize that love couldn't be planned, ordered or categorized—there was no chance for them. And that was why he had to give her this time.

Rubbing his eyes wearily, Michael thought about going home. Leslie would be in Washington by now, probably sitting down to dinner. He winced a little for her sake. He knew she was not looking forward to the evening with her father, and she had enough on her mind without having to drag up the old parental conflicts. He wished he could be there to make it easier for her.

But he didn't feel like going home. Since Leslie had spent the day there, his boat seemed empty, his bed lonely, and all the grand dreams he had once had of life and adventure on the high seas had turned hollow. He decided to work a while longer.

He reached for the latest videotape of the Gaynor twins. This one he had had especially made with infrared light, and if it didn't show him something he didn't know what else to try. Hell, maybe Leslie was right. Maybe these two *did* have something. Miracles, after all, were possible....

THE RESTAURANT her father had chosen was subdued, elegant and tastefully exclusive; that did not surprise Leslie. What did surprise her was that as she was shown to Dr. Roarke's table, two men got to their feet instead of one.

Her father, ageless, distinguished, and impeccably dressed, and another man, blond, attractive, and athletically fit. Leslie's step halted for just a fraction before resuming, and she stifled a moan of dismay and incredulity. Her father, matchmaking? Was it possible?

Leslie had taken particular care with her appearance for the dinner, aware, as always, of some childlike hunger to impress her father. Her black evening pants were svelte and chic, fashionably tapered to a few inches above the ankle and topped by a black crepe overblouse with a deep shawl collar. She wore a spangle of diamondlike jewels in her ears and a matching pendant. Her hair was upswept and piled on top of her head, tilting just a little to shade her left eyebrow. It had been important to her to feel elegant and beautiful tonight; her confidence needed all the bolstering it could get.

Her father's eyes swept over her with evident disapproval, noticing the bright earrings, the partially exposed shoulder, the pants he had specifically asked her not to wear. His lips curled just a fraction in disgust, and when she made a half-movement as though to embrace him in greeting he turned away.

"Leslie," he said, gesturing to the blond man, "I'd like you to meet Dr. Jason Carr. Dr. Carr, my daughter, Leslie."

Leslie, accustomed to disguising the quick hurts her father could inflict so effortlessly upon her, extended her hand to the other man with a warm smile. In the depths of those blue eyes, however, she thought she saw a flicker of kind sympathy, and she liked him without wanting to.

"I've been looking forward to this, Dr. Roarke." His voice was a deep and pleasant baritone, his handclasp warm and firm.

Leslie looked with what she hoped was well-mannered puzzlement to her father. "Oh?"

"Let's sit down," her father said impatiently. "I don't have long."

"I was hoping we'd be able to spend some time together," Leslie said, disappointed even though she knew she should be relieved to escape a three- or four-hour drilling at her father's masterful hands. "We have a lot to catch up on. We haven't seen each other in so long."

"I doubt that anything has occurred in your life that would interest me," her father replied brusquely, "and anything you want to know about me you can pick up in the medical journals."

Leslie caught the inner flesh of her underlip between her teeth, determined not to retort. Why had she expected anything different?

Again she caught a glimpse of kindness in Dr. Carr's eyes, and the gentle smile he gave her was encouraging.

Leslie's father went on, snapping open his napkin, "I ordered for you, Leslie. There's no point wasting time. The only reason I asked you here was to meet Jason. He's a psychiatrist of some renown, as you would know if you had any interest whatsoever in the medical field, and he has a proposition for you."

Leslie looked from her father to Dr. Carr with a gentle lift of her eyebrow. "Therapy?" she suggested, and she wasn't entirely sure she was joking.

Jason laughed softly, shaking his head. His eyes twinkled nicely when he did that. "Actually, no. And I'm sorry to intrude on your reunion with your father; I hate to mix business with pleasure myself. But I'm only in Washington for one night, and I was afraid if I didn't get to meet you now I might not ever have the chance."

"Jason is starting a prototypical substance-abuse clinic in the Detroit area," her father explained, pushing further preliminaries aside. "His program is quite revolutionary and is getting a lot of attention." His impatient slanted glance implied that if she was any kind of professional at all she would know this already. "The Detroit clinic will be the testing ground for a proposed series of privately funded metropolitan treatment centers. He's looking for staff psychologists to train for the program. It sounded like something you would be interested in."

Leslie didn't know what was more astonishing—that her

father would actually take an interest in her career, or that
Dr. Carr would consider her for the position. She tried to
hide her puzzlement as she looked from one man to the
other, and then the soup course arrived. In the moment of
respite she had a chance to form her reply carefully.

"I don't understand," she told Dr. Carr. "This is not
exactly my field—"

"You did drug and alcohol rehabilitation for two years
after you got out of school," her father interrupted shortly,
and picked up his soup spoon.

Leslie was surprised he had remembered. "That was a
long time ago," she told Dr. Carr.

"It doesn't matter," he assured her with a smile. "Some
background in the field is helpful, of course, but what I'm
really looking for are staff members who aren't too inun-
dated with traditional forms of behavioral therapy. My program is so radically different from anything you've ever
learned that a certain amount of open-mindedness is an ab-
solute prerequisite."

So, thought Leslie, *now it's beginning to make sense.* Her
father had heard the words "radical" and "open-minded"
and had immediately thought of her. She supposed she
should have been amused, but she really hadn't the energy
for it tonight. He was still the same as always, still trying
to shuffle his black-sheep daughter into a more respectable
line of work, never bothering to be subtle, never considering what her opinion on the matter was. She had come
here tonight determined not to relent to depression; she was
finding her vow harder to keep than she had imagined.

She wished briefly, intensely, for Michael.

She picked up her soup spoon and said politely to Dr.
Carr, "Tell me about your program."

MICHAEL WATCHED THE TAPE twice, then a third time, and
slowly the satisfaction on his face blossomed into outright
jubilation. He had known it. He had known it all along.

A few swift movements around the room arranged the
proper equipment. He stood a few feet away from the table,

made the undetectable manipulations, then watched as the block of wood burst into flames. He sank back in satisfaction, letting the fire burn itself out on the metal table, dancing orange-and-yellow shadows playing over his face.

And his smile slowly faded. He would have to tell Leslie, of course, and he was not at all sure that this was the best time in her life for her to be proven wrong about something she had just barely come to believe in.

But, he decided with rising spirits, he didn't have to tell her tonight. Tonight he had something far more important to tell her.

LESLIE LAUGHED as the stream of heated brandy felt the touch of the match and burst into flames, casting dancing orange-and-yellow shadows over her face. Her father had not stayed for dessert, which was just as well, because with his disapproving, brooding presence casting a pall over the meal the festive baked Alaska would have been ruined.

She had come here tonight prepared for the stress, expecting disaster, hoping to use the time to put some distance between herself and her confusing feelings about Michael. If there was one thing for which her father could be counted on, it was to consistently remind her what a fool she was. How her father would sneer if she told him she was in love with a magician, shaking his head and muttering that it was no better than he could expect from her. And that was exactly what she needed, a good dose of reality, someone to put everything into perspective for her no matter how much it hurt. The last thing she had expected tonight was to have fun.

Jason must have seen the slight shadow cross her eyes, because he reached out to lay his hand lightly atop hers. "You mustn't be too hard on your father," he said. "He means well. He just has difficulty expressing his feelings, I imagine."

It runs in the family, Leslie thought, and she smiled as she removed her hand. What a nice man Jason was. If she had met him two months ago... "Yes, he means well," she agreed, and her smile turned downward wryly as she picked up her dessert fork. "I suppose in his own mind he has convinced himself that the best thing for me—as well as for him—would be to see me settled in a nice, respectable branch of psychology like the one you're offering. But, Jason—"

He once again deftly cut off the refusal she had been trying to give him all evening. "Actually, I think your work is fascinating," he admitted. "I'd like to hear more about it."

And so, for the remainder of the meal she told him, with glowing avidity in her eyes, of her work at the Center, the possibilities each new case evoked, the things they had learned about the function of the human mind that simply could not have been learned from more orthodox methods of study. She told him about Tony, and her other patients at the hospital. And when he suggested a walk around the city, she did not refuse.

Leslie had decided to stay overnight, knowing that she could not face the two-hour drive back home after a meeting with her father, and hoping, perhaps, that the time alone would give her a chance to sort out her feelings about Michael. If nothing else it would remove from her hands the temptation to simply get in her car and go to him with her emotions unsettled, her mind in turmoil, and the future between them still uncertain...just because she needed to be with him.

Jason and Leslie ended up on the street before her hotel. Conversation and laughter had flowed easily between them, and time passed without notice. Leslie could hardly remember feeling so comfortable with anyone on such short notice, and she had to wonder over that. At this, the most emotionally tumultuous crisis point in her life, in walked a man like Jason, whom she liked on sight, who offered her a job most professionals in her field would have given their eye teeth for, who with a wave of his hand had the power to put everything in Leslie's entire life back in order. Then why wasn't she leaping at the chance? What was missing here?

They stood in the reflected lights of the hotel lobby, and Jason looked down at her with a smile. "All right, I know you've been trying to turn me down all evening. I confess; the only reason I didn't give you a chance was because I thought if I put it off long enough you might change your mind. Have you?"

She laughed softly. "I'm afraid not." And the rational part of her mind demanded indignantly, *For heaven's sake, why not? It's perfect, don't you see that? You'd be crazy to turn it down.* She said, shaking her head slightly, "I guess I must be just as crazy as my father thinks I am but—" she looked up at him "—it's hard to explain, Jason, but what I do is more than a job, more than a practice. There's the challenge, but it's more than that. It's the possibility, every day, of knowing you may stumble into the unknown, pioneer some new frontier, hold the impossible in your hands. It may not be as satisfying or as rewarding as the kind of work you do, and in actual fact it may not be as beneficial to mankind, but... I don't know." She smiled. "I guess part of me was born to take those kinds of chances for minimal rewards. Maybe the only things worth having are the ones acquired at great risk."

He nodded, understanding. "So now you've turned me down professionally." His eyes sobered. "What about personally? I'd like to see you again, Leslie."

Leslie, don't be a fool. He's perfect for you. He's exactly the type of dependable, stable man you need in your life now. He'll keep your feet on the ground. He'll never dazzle you with sleight of hand, or leave you waiting in the dark, or keep a locked chest of secrets that you're not allowed to open. He has nothing to hide. He's good-looking, charming, very likable and easy to understand. He'll make you happy. What more could you ask for?

She smiled at him, a little wistfully. The words were said without her even thinking about them. "Thank you, Jason, but...I don't think so."

He looked at her for another moment, and then he smiled and reached down to brush her lips very lightly with a kiss. "How about if I keep both offers open?"

"Good night, Jason," Leslie said gently and turned to walk inside.

That was when she knew what was missing. The magic.

AS SHE INSERTED THE KEY into her hotel-room lock Leslie's most powerful instinct was to pack her overnight bag, get in her car and drive back to Michael. She could be in his arms before midnight. And wasn't that what love was all about—following one's instincts? Michael had tried to tell her that from the beginning, and she refused to believe it could be that simple. Now she knew.

She stepped inside and flipped on the interior light. Then she stopped, staring.

Every inch of the room was filled with vases of yellow roses.

She whispered, "Michael." And like a phantom summoned from a dream he stepped before her, his sharp, familiar face gentled with uncertainty, his golden eyes softened with a smile and a question. She felt love swell like a bubble inside her, just looking at him.

"Well?" he said softly.

"You were right," she answered. "Thinking didn't help a bit."

She walked into his arms.

THEY LAY TOGETHER shadowed in the spectral street light that streamed through the window, basking in the scent of roses and the aura of lovemaking. Leslie's head lay cradled on Michael's shoulder; her hand traced a slow and lazy pattern from his chest to his hip and she marveled over the wondrous sensation of him. His skin was still damp, his muscles long and lean. He was beautiful to her even in the dark.

"You're a nut, you know," she murmured huskily. "All these roses."

His fingers, which had been cupped quiescently beneath her breast, moved lightly upward, across her throat, trailing affectionately through a swatch of her hair. "I'm not above using whatever advantage I can get to further my cause."

She lifted her face to place a kiss upon the edge of his jaw, dipping her tongue out quickly to taste the saltiness of his skin. She could feel his hands tighten slightly on her shoulder and her own barely quieted desire begin to stir again. She said, "You didn't need extravagant gestures. You already had the advantage." She settled back once again against his shoulder, wanting to savor the moment, knowing that they had plenty of time.

He brushed a kiss across her temple, and she could feel his smile. When he lay against the pillow again there was silence between them for a while, a warm and contented stillness that seemed to be regulated by their synchronous breathing, the slow and steady beat of their hearts.

Then Michael's fingers curved to push a strand of hair behind her ear, and he looked at her face in the dimness. "Was it very bad," he asked, "with your father?"

Leslie smiled to herself. She had spoken to Michael very little about her father, had in fact only mentioned him once, but it was part of the mystical nature of Michael's personality that he would understand. It was part of the reason she loved him.

"It's my own fault, you know," she said thoughtfully, reaching her hand up to link it with his. "I let them work on my confidence. I always feel as though I have something to prove, and my parents manipulate that."

"Leslie, you're an established professional. You do thorough, respected work. You shouldn't feel like you're competing with anyone."

Gratefully, she let her fingers brush across his lips. "But I am, you know. I may be good at what I do, but I'm not brilliant. My parents are brilliant, and they hold their accomplishments in front of my nose like a carrot on a stick, hoping I'll be motivated to follow them. Only it doesn't work like that. Instead I'm so afraid of making a mistake that I won't go forward, won't commit to anything, won't take the very chances that *make* brilliance. I always wanted to," she added thoughtfully. "I just didn't know how." She turned her face to look up at him. "Until you."

"Leslie," he said a little hoarsely, and even in the uncertain light she could see the yearning on his face, feel it in the naked muscles that tensed, ever so slightly, against hers. "I'm not the one to take lessons on commitment from. The problems we've had are as much my fault as they are yours, and darling, I'm just as frightened of making a mistake as you are. The only thing," he said softly, "that I've ever wanted to commit to is you."

Leslie wrapped her arm around his shoulder, pressing her face to his warm, damp chest, briefly, intensely. "Don't you see, Michael?" she said, lifting her eyes to his again. "Maybe you didn't mean to, but by being so..." Her lips tightened with a smile. "Obstinate, and impossible and frustrating—you forced me to find out what I really wanted and to take a stand to defend it. You made me see," she told him gently, "that what I wanted was a miracle, and you gave it to me. You made me believe in all sorts of things...like magic, and poltergeists—" her eyes sparked briefly with a teasing smile, then sobered "—and you. That was all I ever really wanted."

His arms slipped around her, drawing her partially on top of him; he kissed her deeply. Lifting his hands to stroke away her forward-falling hair, he inquired softly, "Is that enough?"

Leslie smiled, resting her arms on either side of his head as she leaned over him. Her finger slipped out to trace the shape of his hairline and his nose, and he caught his breath as her touch glanced over his lips. "My father even went to the trouble to arrange a job for me. A nice, steady, secure position in a very respected, exciting new field. In Detroit, with one of the most innovative young psychiatrists in the country."

She felt him hesitate, his fingers resting lightly on the tip of her spine. "And?"

"And—" she leaned forward to drop a kiss upon his lips "—I didn't even have to think about it. I've got everything I want right here."

She felt his smile against her face, saw the golden sparks in his eyes as reflected by the streetlight. His fingers curled around her buttocks, shifting her weight slightly, positioning her. She gasped softly with the sensation, her heart beginning a heavy, sonorous rhythm of anticipation.

"Can it be," he inquired lightly, "that you're letting your emotions interfere with your judgment?"

"That's exactly," she whispered, "what I'm doing. And it's..." She caught her breath, letting her eyes drift closed with the slow, filling pleasure as he slid into her. "Wonderful."

Chapter Thirteen

Leslie awoke the next morning to two uncomfortable sensations—the light streaming into her eyes, and the babble of a morning news show coming from the television screen. She groaned and rolled over, pulling a pillow over her head.

And then there was one very pleasant sensation: Michael, kneeling astride her, his lips nuzzling the back of her neck, his hair tickling her bare shoulder. "I have only one bad habit," he murmured into her ear, "but I think you should know about it before we go any further. I'm very much a morning person."

"I know," Leslie muttered, smiling into her pillow. "I seem to recall you were at your best about four o'clock this morning."

"Was I?" He stretched out beside her, grinning, taking a strand of her hair and tickling her under the chin until she rolled over, doing her best to glare at him.

"I'm *not* a morning person," she warned him severely.

"Here." He stretched out an arm and in another moment the steamy aroma of coffee greeted her nostrils. "This will make up for it. Room service."

Leslie gave an appreciative moan and sat up, taking the cup from him. "You do have some redeeming virtues, after all."

She pushed her hair away from her face, letting the sheet fall down around her bare breasts as she did so. Michael's fingers came out automatically to caress the shape lightly, tantalizingly, with the familiar ease of affection that made Leslie smile, remembering how much they had shared together in such a short time. The feeling of belonging she had with him defied description or explanation and logically it should not have been so, but it was there. As though they had been bonded forever, and had spent all of their lives waiting for time to bring them together.

He had pulled on his jeans but not his shirt, and it was a very great temptation for Leslie to stretch out her hand and place her palm against his heartbeat, to trace the smoothly defined muscles of breast and torso with her fingers. She wanted to close her eyes and make endless, drowsy love to him, and at the same time she wanted to sit, cozy and relaxed with him, and just sip her coffee and share the morning. She had never imagined that life's choices could be so intensely pleasurable.

He said, "Are we going back today, or shall we stay and enjoy the sights of the big city together?"

Leslie, slanting a glance at him beneath her lashes, thought they would be staying a few more hours, at least.

"We should get back," she murmured, without much enthusiasm. "I have appointments today. We both have work to do."

His eyes sparked with quick affection and he leaned forward to drop a kiss on her lips. "Responsible to the end, Dr. Roarke. You're very good for me."

He pushed himself off the bed and started toward the bathroom.

"How did you get here?" she asked, wondering if they might drive back together.

He paused and winked at her. "By broomstick."

Leslie chuckled, and sipped her coffee. The room looked like a fairyland with all the roses, and she wanted to take them all back with her. The scent was heavenly, like a dream that hadn't quite ended yet, and when she heard the shower start she thought lazily about getting up and joining Michael. And then she thought what she really wanted to do was to lie here and wait for him, and then to make love in the midst of the bright morning sunshine and all these roses.

But then she thought about Michael, his body sleek and wet and slippery beneath her fingers, the steamy warmth, the sting of the water, the taste of him, and she didn't want to wait at all. She flung back the covers and reached for her robe.

Then something on the television caught her attention.

"...Kevin and Karen Gaynor, who've caused quite a stir in the scientific world with their demonstration of what can only be described as extraordinary psychic powers..."

Leslie stared as the camera switched to the twins, sitting on the set of the national news show, looking relaxed and at ease as they focused their attention on the interviewer.

"Tell us something about yourselves. As I understand, what you have is something like a psychic link...."

Kevin spoke. "That's right. Neither one of us seems to be much good without the other...."

"Michael!" Leslie cried.

But he had already seen. He stood at the door of the bathroom, a white towel wrapped around his waist, his jaw tense and his face a little pale.

"...understand you have been the object of considerable intensive observation at the—" the interviewer consulted her notes "—Center for the Study of Psi and Related Phenomena in Maryland. What have they been able to..."

"Who the hell authorized this?" Michael demanded harshly.

"I—I don't know," Leslie replied weakly, staring at the set. "No one, I guess. They couldn't have, without my approval." But hadn't she known it? That day Karen had seemed so preoccupied with "making a profit," the way both of them thrived on attention. She should have known they wouldn't keep their secrets to themselves very long.

"I wonder if you would be willing to demonstrate..."

Michael, swearing viciously, strode over to the television

set and snapped it off. For a moment he paced the room tensely and Leslie, her mind whirling, said nothing.

"By the time we get back to the Center the place will be crawling with reporters," Michael said shortly, after a moment. He ran his hand through his wet hair with a tense, angry gesture and hissed, "Damn!"

"I'd better call Winston," Leslie said briskly, reaching for the telephone. "Though I doubt whether he knows any more about this than we do."

"How could a thing like this happen?" Michael demanded, though more to himself than to Leslie. "This will be the media cause for the month, and when they find out about the grant—"

"Maybe it's not so bad," Leslie tried to reassure herself, punching out the numbers. Of course she hated to be taken by surprise like this, but maybe this was exactly the impetus they all needed to make their research public. If it weren't for her own cautious nature, her refusal to take chances, they would have done so long before this. The twins couldn't be blamed for taking matters into their own hands.

"I mean," she went on, "we can only keep it to ourselves so long, and we all knew time was running out. This *is* what the Center needs, to let the public know what kind of work we're doing, to open our research to the scrutiny of the general public as well as the scientific community. The Gaynors are the most exciting thing to happen to psychic research in decades; we all know that, and there's no point in keeping quiet about it forever. Of course, I would have preferred—"

Then she happened to glance at Michael. His face was grim, his eyes dark with turmoil and reluctance, and Leslie felt a chill go through her that seemed to penetrate her very core. She said, barely forcing her dry throat to form the words, "You found out how they did it, didn't you?"

Michael stood there for the longest time. The phone, in the midst of its connection, grew clammy in Leslie's hand while it waited for her to punch in the final digit. And Michael, tense, alert, pained, finally nodded.

"I have it on tape," he said. His voice was quiet but it seemed to ring through the morning-bright, rose-filled room. "No mistake. No room for doubt. They were using a light-sensitive ignition device, parts available in any hardware store, skills available from any science text. The only reason I didn't see it before was because it was so simple."

Leslie let the phone slip from her numbed fingers back onto its hook. For an endless moment she could think of nothing; her entire consciousness seemed to be shrouded in a thick, immobilizing fog and at the center of it all was Michael's face, hard, remote and expressionless. Waiting.

Then, abruptly, the fog was lifted. The implications exploded on her all at once, with stinging rapidity and crippling clarity, so quickly that she hardly had time to grasp the significance of one truth before another was bombarding her. She had been wrong. She had believed; for the first time she had taken a stand and believed that they had found the genuine article—but she had been fooled, tricked, just as easily and just as thoroughly as Michael had fooled her that first day. She had made a mistake. She hadn't been cautious enough, thorough enough, precise enough, and she had been wrong.

The scandal. What would happen to the Center when this got out? What would happen to the entire field of research? In almost thirty years of methodical, conservative, scientifically careful work, their reputation had remained impeccable. Nothing like this had ever touched them before. How would they deal with this?

This was just the sort of thing her father had always expected from her. To be exposed as a fraud, centered in scandal, the laughing stock of the professional community. What would happen to her career after this? Would she even have a career left?

How could she have been so wrong? *Letting your emotions influence your judgment, Leslie?* She had wanted to believe in the Gaynors, and she had. It was as simple, as stupid, as unprofessional and as blind as that. She had wanted so badly to prove Michael wrong. She had wanted so badly to believe in something.

She looked up at Michael. "You knew," she accused. Her voice was shaking. "You knew all along."

"I told you that. I told you from the beginning—"

"But you didn't tell me *why*!" She pulled on her robe with jerky fingers, getting to her feet. "You wouldn't tell any of us why! You with your damn ethics and your professional secrets! You kept stalling for time and keeping us in the dark."

"I couldn't say anything until I could prove it." His voice was very quiet. Too quiet. Not a muscle in his body moved. "That was the deal."

"You didn't give us anything to work with! Damn it, I was their *counselor*! If I had even a hint of what you were working on, of what they were doing, I could have worked with you—all of this could have been prevented!" She was only a few feet away from him now, her color high, her eyes blazing. "You should have told me! You were so damn close-mouthed and evasive none of us knew whether to believe you or not! We didn't have the first idea—"

"You should have trusted me."

The words were clipped, short and effective. They went straight through Leslie's chest and left her breathless. That, of course, was the essence of it all. If she had trusted him instead of fighting him, if he had trusted her enough to share his theories with her...

Michael released a breath; he half turned from her and ran his hand through his hair again, and this time it was a tired gesture. "All right. Maybe I should have told you what I was trying to do; maybe it would have helped you to know why I thought they were faking. I'm just not used to working that way; I'm used to people taking it for granted that I'm the only one who knows the secrets. I should have known you would have to have diagrams drawn." There was no venom to the words, only resignation, and he looked at her plainly. "But none of that matters now, does it? It's done."

Yes, it was done. And all they could do now was try to salvage what they could. Leslie looked at him hesitantly. "What are you going to do?"

She saw it in his eyes, the reflection of her own thoughts, the possibilities and the impossibilities that were left to them. Michael held all their futures in his hands. If he could keep silent, if he could let Leslie and Malcolm and George handle the twins, if they could make sure this thing stopped now, before it got any bigger, no more publicity... If Michael would just give them a chance, maybe they could handle this quietly....

But how *could* they keep it quiet? Michael was right; even now half the press of the free world was swooping down on the Center, nothing short of an act of God—or a statement from Michael Bradshaw—would stop the eyes of the world from turning to the Gaynor twins as the true, living evidence of psychic phenomena. But if he exposed the twins for what he knew them to be, they all would be ruined. Not just Leslie, and George and Malcolm and the Center, but everything they had dedicated their lives to. Other researchers they didn't even know would be affected by this. It would take years, and then some, for the field of psychic research to recover from this blow. No one associated with this project would ever be taken seriously again.

And as all of this and more went through her head, she saw Michael's face slowly tighten with the pain, the dread of what he was about to do—not only to the Center, but to Leslie and to himself. His voice was hoarse as he said, "I have to tell the truth. I have no choice."

The sound of his own words and the consequences that went with them were like a knife twisting deep in his stomach. All his life he had sought the truth, treasured the truth, held it close to him like a treasured talisman. Now the truth was destroying the woman he loved and he was the bearer of the blow. Leslie, so fragile, so vulnerable, so cautious, had believed in him and he had betrayed her. Leslie, who could not afford to make mistakes, had just made the biggest mistake of her life and there was nothing he could do to shield her from it. More than professional goals and reputations were at stake here; he knew that. The very core of her newfound confidence was shaken, and it was a blow from which she might never recover. And all because he had to tell the truth.

A shudder gripped Leslie profoundly, and she closed her hands around her elbows to steady herself against it. It sank in then, heavily. "I should have known," she whispered dully. "They were my patients and I should have known. How could I have been so wrong?"

She raised eyes to Michael that were dark with sorrow and dread, and he knew exactly what she was thinking. She had been wrong about this. What else had she been wrong about?

He ached to pull her into his arms, to comfort her, to tell her everything was going to be all right. But he made no move, and the effort to restrain himself stung like tears in the back of his throat. He had no comfort to offer. And he was not at all sure everything was going to be all right. He was afraid, in fact, that nothing would be right ever again.

After a long time his voice came, low and strained. He could not meet her eyes. "We'd better get moving. We've got a hard fight ahead."

Leslie responded bleakly, "Yes."

And they both knew that this time they would be fighting on opposite sides, and neither one would emerge the victor.

LESLIE KNEW that it would be a nightmare, but nothing could have prepared her for what lay ahead in the next two weeks. The first thing the Center did was issue a disclaimer regarding any support of claims made by Karen and Kevin Gaynor. It would have been naively optimistic to imagine the circus would end there. Kevin and Karen hotly asserted to weeks of research within the Center that proved their ability beyond a doubt. Michael made a statement to the press. The Gaynors denied it, and promptly filed suit against Michael Bradshaw and the Center for slander and libel.

There was an investigation into government involvement. The government discreetly withdrew its funding and denied ever having heard of the Center. Half the board members resigned, afraid of the publicity. Kevin and Karen went on talk shows. Michael went on talk shows. Leslie stopped watching television.

Leslie gave interviews, desperately trying to preserve the Center's integrity by explaining that erroneous results of their research had been announced prematurely, that Michael Bradshaw had been hired by the Center to protect against just such occurrences of fraud, that they were a carefully regulated scientific program that could not be held responsible for unvalidated claims by volunteer subjects. Perhaps some of it helped. But in print all she saw was, "Dr. Leslie Roarke, daughter of imminent cardiologist Amos Roarke and noted genetic engineer Margaret Douglas..."

Neither of her parents called to offer to stand by her in her time of need. The best she could hope for was that rumors of the troubles of the prodigal child of science did not make their way upward to the ivory tower of the socially elite. She didn't think she could deal with her parents now.

She didn't see Michael in person again. She knew he was trying to avoid the spotlight as much as possible, and he was doing his best to keep attention away from the Center. When asked for a response to a claim made by the Gaynors, he gave it. When the Gaynors did a television interview, he countered it. To do less would have been dishonest and unethical. But when asked about the Center, he was always careful to exonerate them from any responsibility for negligence, and then changed the subject. Leslie blessed him for that, but it made little difference.

Michael couldn't be blamed for what had happened and she didn't try. He had been brought to the Center to aid in their joint quest for the truth; he had only done his job. She knew that he had not deliberately betrayed her; Leslie had betrayed herself.

She couldn't exonerate herself from her responsibility in the affair. The Gaynors had been her patients; she had known exactly what they were capable of. All the clues were there in her files: unstable personalities, exaggerated interdependency, insecurity and a need for reassurance. The intelligence, skills and capacity for deception. At any other time she would have earmarked that file for special attention; she would have proceeded very, very carefully. But she had had something to prove. To Michael, to herself. She had ignored the warning signs and dedicated herself wholeheartedly to supporting the twins. She had led with her heart and not her mind, and she had made a mistake.

It was toward the beginning of the third week that some of the publicity began to die down. Kevin and Karen were learning just how fickle the public could be, and already the media had embraced some new darling, some more challenging cause. About that same time an article appeared in one of the widely circulated weekly news magazines delineating just how easily some of the more common claims by charlatan psychics could be exposed. It was written by Michael Bradshaw.

Shortly after that, word came that Karen and Kevin had dropped their lawsuit. Leslie began to breathe a cautious sigh of relief.

And then her father called.

He was brief and to the point. "I'm not going to say I didn't warn you. You know perfectly well that this is exactly the sort of thing I predicted would happen years ago, and all I have to say on the subject is that it's best it happened now, while you're still young enough to recover from the blow and get on with your life."

That was the closest, Leslie knew, that she would ever come to hearing an expression of sympathy from her father, and she was oddly touched. She said, "I'm sorry I disappointed you, Daddy."

There was a brief and poignant silence, and in it father and daughter came close to touching a bond neither of them expected. And then her father blustered, "Disappointed me? Don't be absurd. You're a bright young woman, Leslie, I've always known that, and to be perfectly frank I think you've handled this entire distasteful matter with considerable aplomb. The best thing to do now is put it behind you. Have you called Jason yet?''

For a moment the name didn't ring a bell, and Leslie hesitated. ''Oh, you mean Dr. Carr?''

''Of course I mean Dr. Carr. It's the best thing that could happen to you right now—start all over in a new field. All in all, I'd say things worked out quite well, wouldn't you?''

Leslie smiled sadly, shaking her head a little against the receiver. ''I don't know what makes you think Dr. Carr would want me anymore. I haven't shown the best of judgment; I've gotten my name splashed all over the papers; I made a grave professional error. And none of that looks very good on a resume.''

''Number one,'' her father returned curtly, ''you're taking this whole thing much more seriously than it warrants—and more seriously than anyone else is, I can assure you. Number two—you made a mistake. It's not the first and it won't be the last.'' He laughed, and it was a gruff, unfamiliar sound to Leslie. ''Hell, do you think you're the first person it ever happened to? What do you think penicillin was? A mistake, that's what, an accident, pure and simple. And let me tell you something, young lady, making a mistake now and then is the best thing that can happen to you—it teaches you not to get too cocky. You learn to take chances, and you learn to live with yourself when you fail. You learn to try again, and you learn not to waste your life trying so hard to be perfect that you're never anything at all. I'm not saying that if you had it to do all over again that I'd want you to make the same choices, but this just might be the best thing that ever happened to you. I think you'll see things a lot more clearly now.''

Leslie did begin to see things more clearly—not all at once, but by degrees. As the week wore on and she replayed in her head that longest and most significant conversation she and her father had ever had, she began to understand a lot of things about herself, about her father, about her choices.

Several times she'd had her hand on the telephone to call Jason Carr. Perhaps her father was right. Maybe it was time to give up the dreams, to pick up the pieces of her life and move on. The Center was in dire financial straits; it was questionable whether they would be able to secure the funding to stay open another year. So far, the board of the children's hospital had been sympathetic and understanding and were genuinely desirous that she stay; it would be hard to leave her patients there. But there was just as much personal and professional satisfaction to be found in the type of work Jason offered, and just as much challenge. And so she thought, more and more seriously every day, about calling Jason Carr. But somehow she never did.

She realized, somewhere in the midst of all this, that she was waiting for Michael to call her. She wanted to call him, but she didn't know what to say. He had told her once that she had to accept him on faith, just as he was, but she felt so bruised and shaken inside, so battered by the events that had torn them apart these past weeks, that she was no longer confident in her ability to make any kind of commitment—not to a new job, not to the Center, which needed her more desperately than it ever had, not even to herself. And she could not to go Michael unsure.

And then, abruptly, something happened that made her blindly, unthinkingly sure.

Since Michael had uncovered the secret to Tony's language, Tony's therapy was progressing by leaps and bounds. He still couldn't speak in the accepted sense of the word, but they had learned to communicate with him by recording his speech and playing it back in slow reverse. Being able to finally communicate, instead of simply being spoken to and shouting back words no one could understand, made a drastic difference in Tony's behavior. He was calmer, more attentive, and made a more concentrated effort to cooperate. People were listening to him now. He was beginning to feel as though he belonged in their world.

The first thing Leslie played back after Tony's enthusiastic greeting at their afternoon session was, "Michael wanted to say goodbye to you. He misses you. He's sailing away to the Virgin Islands. He wishes you would come with him."

Leslie's heart missed a beat, and her breath stopped for half a second. The tape, slowed down as it was, was not entirely clear, and she thought perhaps she had misunderstood. She said to Tony very clearly, "What did you say? Slowly, please."

Tony had never had any trouble understanding Leslie. He repeated his previous speech, word for word, making a concentrated effort to speak more slowly.

Leslie played it back, her heart thumping in her ears. "When did you see Michael?"

Tony chattered something that she could hardly wait to play back. It was "Michael wanted to say goodbye to you. He misses you. He's sailing away...."

Leslie waited until the tape had finished playing before she demanded, "When, Tony? When is Michael leaving?"

He said something, very carefully, very soberly. She played it back. "Today. Goodbye forever."

LESLIE'S HEART DIDN'T STOP its frantic, crazed beating all through the endless drive to the dock. Today. He was leaving today without a word. Why should he say anything? They had said it all that morning in a hotel room filled with yellow roses and the echo of disaster. She hadn't been concerned for him then, for what he might be going through; she hadn't had a thought for anyone but herself. She hadn't asked him to stay. She hadn't even spoken to him throughout this whole horrible ordeal, had made no effort to contact him. What if she was too late? What if he had already left?

Goodbye forever....

The August sun beat down on her unmercifully as she left her car and ran down the pier. She was too late. She knew she was. Why had she waited so long? What had she been *thinking* about?

Her heart caught in her throat for a moment as she saw, unmistakably, the gleaming white hull of the *Annabelle Lee*, and then started racing again frantically, wondrously. She slowed her steps, trying to breathe, trying to believe that Fate could have been so kind.

He was standing on deck, wearing white jeans and an unbuttoned denim shirt that billowed away from his bare chest with the occasional breeze. He was half-turned from her, bending over something on the deck, and for the moment she had to simply stand there watching him. *Oh, God, Michael.* The plea swelled up her chest with an ache that came from her very soul. *Please want me.....*

With all the courage she possessed, she called out, "Permission to come aboard, sir?"

Michael straightened slowly and turned. He looked at her for the longest moment with nothing but naked disbelief in his eyes. And then he said softly, hardly more than a breath, "Leslie."

She didn't wait for permission. She couldn't afford to wait. She crossed the small ramp and leaped to the deck. A moment too late, Michael shook off his daze and extended his hand to help her, then, finding her standing before him, let it drop uncertainly.

He still looked at her as though he couldn't believe his eyes. He said after a moment, "I didn't expect to see you again."

Leslie linked her hands tightly together before her; it was the only way to stop the trembling. She was glad the sun caused her to squint as she looked into his eyes, otherwise he surely would have seen the pleading there. She said, very precisely, "I've been thinking, and I discovered something very interesting about myself. I thought you might like to know what it was."

The breeze gently ruffled his sun-drenched hair. His eyes went over her busily, anxiously, but his face was expressionless, unreadable. "What?"

She took a breath. "That I don't make commitments often, but when I do...they're forever." She saw the brief flare of question, of hope in his eyes, and she went on in a rush, "Michael, I love you. I didn't know how much until I thought I might lose you and there wasn't time to think anymore. I just knew that I loved you and I couldn't bear to let you go...."

But then her words were buried in his chest; his arms were crushingly tight around her; the roar of his heartbeat filled her ears and she could feel the muscles of his arms tremble. "Leslie," he whispered breathlessly, "I knew if I didn't leave I wouldn't be able to stay away from you. I knew how hurt you were, and confused, and I couldn't pressure you to accept me when I knew what you were going through."

Slowly, with agonizing reluctance, his embrace loosened. He pushed her a little away, his fingers wrapped around her forearms, his eyes sober as he looked into hers. "Leslie," he said quietly, "I do love you. I want to spend the rest of my life proving how much I love you, but I'm not sure I can. I've spent so much of my life keeping secrets that it's not easy for me to share myself with someone else. And I'm not saying I can change. I know how important it is for you to be sure of people and of things around you, to understand what makes everything work. Maybe you'll never understand me, and maybe I won't make it any easier, and sometimes we'll both be frightened. All I can promise is that I won't stop loving you."

"Oh, Michael," she whispered, and pressed her face to his chest again. "That's all I need."

They kissed, drenched in the glory of the sun, bodies and minds and souls meeting and blending, and when they came apart, each was dazed, wondering, renewed. Leslie lifted her hands to cup his face, her eyes dancing with invitation. "And now, Mr. Bradshaw, about this voyage of yours. How do you feel about taking on a passenger?"

He pretended to think about it. "I'm sorry, but my space is limited. I have room only for one world-weary psychologist in need of a rest."

"What a coincidence. I happen to know just such a person."

"The accommodations aren't deluxe," he warned her. "You'd have to share your bed."

She leaned toward him. "I wouldn't have it any other way."

He caught her to him, laughing into her hair. "God, Leslie, this almost makes me believe in Fate. If you had been an hour later, you would have missed me."

She nodded against his chest, holding him tight. "If Tony hadn't told me, I wouldn't have come at all. I needed that shock, I think, to put things in perspective."

He stepped back a fraction, his expression puzzled. "Tony? How did he know?"

"Why—" Leslie looked up at him curiously "—you told him."

Something strange crossed Michael's face, and she felt it reflected in her own chest. "Leslie..." he said slowly, "I didn't tell Tony anything. I haven't seen him since the last time I was there with you."

They stared at each other. Leslie managed, "Then how did he...?"

But, looking at each other, they both knew there was no answer to that question.

As the wonder slowly filled her, Michael caught her to him, chuckling softly with joy and amazement. "I think, Dr. Roarke," he said, "we both have a lot to learn. And—" he tilted her face upward to receive his kiss "—the best part has only begun."

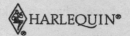

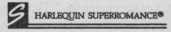

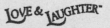

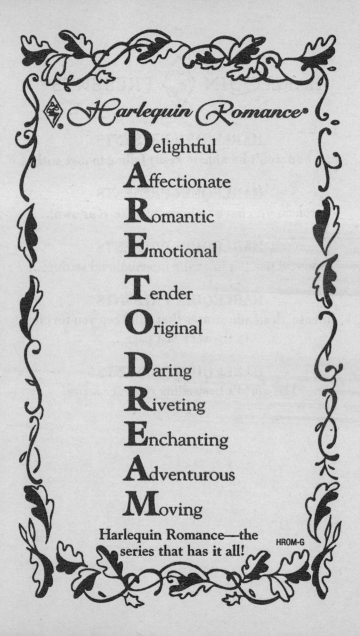

Harlequin Romance®

Delightful

Affectionate

Romantic

Emotional

Tender

Original

Daring

Riveting

Enchanting

Adventurous

Moving

Harlequin Romance—the
series that has it all!

HROM-G

HARLEQUIN PRESENTS®

HARLEQUIN PRESENTS
men you won't be able to resist falling in love with...

HARLEQUIN PRESENTS
women who have feelings just like your own...

HARLEQUIN PRESENTS
powerful passion in exotic international settings...

HARLEQUIN PRESENTS
intense, dramatic stories that will keep you turning
to the very last page...

HARLEQUIN PRESENTS
The world's bestselling romance series!

S HARLEQUIN SUPERROMANCE®

...there's more to the story!

Superromance. A *big* satisfying read about unforgettable characters. Each month we offer *four* very different stories that range from family drama to adventure and mystery, from highly emotional stories to romantic comedies—and much more! Stories about people you'll believe in and care about. Stories too compelling to put down....

Our authors are among today's *best* romance writers. You'll find familiar names and talented newcomers. Many of them are award winners—and you'll see why!

If you want the biggest and best in romance fiction, you'll get it from Superromance!
Available wherever Harlequin books are sold.

LOOK FOR OUR FOUR FABULOUS MEN!

Each month some of today's bestselling authors bring four new fabulous men to Harlequin American Romance. Whether they're rebel ranchers, millionaire power brokers or sexy single dads, they're all gallant princes—and they're all ready to sweep you into lighthearted fantasies and contemporary fairy tales where anything is possible and where all your dreams come true!

You don't even have to make a wish...Harlequin American Romance will grant your every desire!

Look for Harlequin American Romance wherever Harlequin books are sold!

Harlequin® Historical

If you're a serious fan of historical romance,
then you're in luck!

Harlequin Historicals brings you
stories by bestselling authors, rising new stars
and talented first-timers.

Ruth Langan & Theresa Michaels
Mary McBride & Cheryl St.John
Margaret Moore & Merline Lovelace
Julie Tetel & Nina Beaumont
Susan Amarillas & Ana Seymour
Deborah Simmons & Linda Castle
Cassandra Austin & Emily French
Miranda Jarrett & Suzanne Barclay
DeLoras Scott & Laurie Grant…

You'll never run out of favorites.

Harlequin Historicals…they're too good to miss!

HH-GEN